CHANGING THE WORLD'S EXERCISE HABITS

Changing The World's Exercise Habits:

A History Of Dr. Kenneth Cooper's Fitness Missionaries

TOM COLLINGWOOD

ROGER REYNOLDS

JOHN POTEET

Charleston, SC
www.PalmettoPublishing.com

Changing The World's Exercise Habits
Copyright © 2021 by Tom Collingwood | Roger Reynolds | John Poteet

Paperback: 978-1-63837-773-3
Hardcover: 978-1-63837-774-0
eBook: 978-1-63837-775-7

Table of Contents

Foreword

It has been said that any CEO is going to be just as successful as his staff makes him. That is why I say after fifty-one years developing the Cooper Aerobics Center, I believe my success can be attributed to (1) divine intervention and (2) a fantastic staff! Nothing could exemplify this feeling more accurately than what you will read in this book.

I call them the "terrific trio." Tom, Roger, and John not only talked the talk but also walked/ran it in a remarkable and most professional way.

Tom was the leader, particularly with his US Army experience as a paratrooper with the famous 82nd Airborne Division. Roger was close behind with the inspirational and motivational leadership he developed as a wide receiver with the NFL football team the New York Giants. And then John was the dedicated, highly disciplined academic of the group who instilled teaching and coaching talents in the other two.

For over thirty years, the contributions that this group made to the Continuing Education Division of the Cooper Institute were legendary. Their accomplishments included working with the US military, police and patrol officers, teachers and school administrators, pastors, and even children. In all these endeavors literally all over the world, they achieved unbelievable success. To this day, I still receive accolades about what these men accomplished.

But what I appreciate most is the strong Christian faith that is evident throughout this book. As John Poteet says, it was "providence" that led him to the Cooper Institute and that their group was protected as they traveled the world, on many occasions having to overcome obstacles such as flight changes and delays, adaptation to different time zones, and even fatigue from not only lecturing but also the physical requirements of exercising with students when testing their fitness.

As I look back over the "glory years" of the Continuing Education Division of the Cooper Institute, it makes me sad that we are no longer active in that field. With over seven hundred publications coming from the Cooper Institute, we now have a world of new data to provide to students that proves that "exercise is medicine." With a database of over 125,000 patients, over 300,000 maximal performance treadmill stress tests, and in excess of 1 million personal follow-ups on these patients, it is the most comprehensive database in the world proving that "exercise is medicine." And it has frequently been said that "when something comes from the Cooper Institute about how much exercise is enough," the whole world listens!

I have hopes that in the future, cooperating with ACE (American Council on Exercise), we will again be establishing our fitness specialist programs (which I personally enjoyed participating in) and, with new, highly motivated, and qualified professionals, renew our consultation services to all types of people and professional groups as we were doing in the past. However, without the "terrific trio" of Tom, Roger, and John, I doubt we will ever be able to accomplish what they did as is clearly documented in this book.

Kenneth H. Cooper, MD, MPH

Founder and Chairman, The Cooper Institute/Cooper Clinic/Cooper Aerobics Enterprises, Inc./Cooper Wellness Strategies

Preface

This book is dedicated to all the staff who were involved in the work of the Cooper Aerobics Center over the years. There has not been a finer group of committed professionals who accomplished many impossible "missions" in the field of physical fitness.

We express a special gratitude to Dr. Kenneth Cooper, whose vision and leadership enabled the Cooper Aerobics Center to be the premier preventive medicine and fitness model for the entire world. Likewise, his mentorship of the entire center's staff made it possible for the energetic and missionary outreach of programs and services to flourish. He is without question the pioneer whose giant footsteps left a trail for us to follow.

Introduction

The purpose of this book is to tell a story. It is a unique story of a mission and missionaries, not in the context of a religious purpose, but something else. That something else is a mission to help others to develop a physically active lifestyle that has profound implications for their health and well-being for a fuller and expanded longevity.

It is a story of what happens when a visionary creates a center (mission) and develops a staff (team of missionaries) who are committed, with high energy, to apply the missionary goal worldwide. It is not so much a story of the ultimate results of the effort but more of the process and the people who made it happen.

Dr. Kenneth Cooper, often called the "Father of Aerobics," developed an exercise system in the late 1960s that revolutionized the America's and the world's exercise habits. It was a system who's most prominent symbol at the time was the jogger, even though the aerobics point system he developed could be applied to any type of exercise. The public's exercise habits doubled as his program became popular.

Beyond the exercise system, Dr. Cooper had a much broader vision. It was one of exercise functioning as preventive medicine, especially for those diseases due to inactivity, such as heart disease. It was also a vision of applying not just exercise, but other lifestyle factors, such as nutrition, to increase one's total health and well-being. For that vision to happen, he recognized the need for a place and an outreach effort. As a result, in the 1970s he established the Cooper Aerobics Center in

Dallas, Texas, and the succeeding years saw outreach efforts for exercise and fitness appear with worldwide effects.

The major outreach vehicle was the Cooper Institute (originally named the Institute for Aerobics Research). It was one of the Cooper Aerobics Center's three main entities, whose mission it was to conduct research into the effects of fitness and exercise on overall well-being and then transfer that learning into educational and other service programs. This is a story of his vision becoming a positive force for health through the Cooper Institute's efforts, especially its Continuing Education Division.

This book is not intended to be a comprehensive history of all the efforts, labors, and achievements of the Cooper Aerobics Center and Cooper Institute. As a consequence, some of the initiatives and efforts are not referenced or explored. The story we are telling is but the historical reflections and memoirs of Dr. Tom Collingwood, Roger Reynolds, M.A., and Dr. John Poteet as we have entered into our later years of our life's work at the Cooper Institute. It is the remembrances of our personal experiences where we expended considerable energy engaging in projects and services that we were heavily committed to and involved with over an approximately thirty-five-year span with the Cooper Institute. That reflection led us to recognize that we had a strong purpose and zeal for all our efforts and, as a consequence, led us to frame our work as "missionary" outreaches, and that term will be used throughout the telling of our story. While much of the story is about our personal involvement, it is also, at the same time, a story about the team of "missionary" professionals within the Cooper Aerobics Center, which we were a part of.

This story will first provide (in Section I) a brief background on the lack of full acceptance and practice of an active physical lifestyle prior to what many have called the "Cooper revolution." Next, an overview will be provided of Dr. Cooper's work and vision leading to the development of the Cooper Aerobics Center concept as a mission with a missionary outreach. Section II will then tell the story of the various projects and programs ("missionary activities") we were involved in.

Finally, the learning and implications from the various "missionary" efforts will be discussed.

In this day and age of dissension, anger, lack of common goals, backbiting, personal agendas, and divisions over every conceivable trait and viewpoint, a story of what happens when you have a different way is sorely needed in our current times. It is story of a diversity of fitness and health professionals from different backgrounds and with different skills but with two common denominators. The first was that physical activity and an active lifestyle were key traits that defined the core of their being. Secondly, they had developed skills and a burning desire to help others become fully active and fit for total well-being. In that context, we will provide a brief glimpse into the history of the three of us, as examples, of the staff (missionaries) who worked within the Cooper Aerobics Center that will provide a perspective for that personal "missionary" commitment and teamwork.

If you are interested in learning more about a success story—especially how committed people working as a team can make a difference—or, more specifically, if you want to learn more about how helping others to be physically active and fit can translate into a variety of human benefits, then this will be a story for you. Enjoy.

SECTION I:
Creation of a "Mission"

Before exploring the concept of the Cooper Aerobics Center as a "mission" and its service activities as "missionary outreaches," a foundation needs to be laid. That foundation or historical background relates to the need for exercise and the resultant physical fitness movement, the pioneering work of Dr. Kenneth Cooper in addressing the needs of preventive medicine and fitness, and his eventual establishment of the Cooper Aerobics Center.

Organizational psychologists have attempted to define the necessary ingredients for an organization to accomplish its goals and function fully, and they often provide highly detailed elements. The Human Technology group provided perhaps the simplest and most clear description of the ingredients as consisting of just three major factors: people, programs, and organizational structure/support. The nature of physical fitness and the physical domain of exercise and activity highlight the importance of the "people" factor. Modeling, instruction, energy, and motivation are key elements to aid others in changing their movement habits. To be more precise, it is a "leadership factor," and it is the lion's share of the variance of success, and this was certainly the case for the Cooper Aerobics Center.

Leadership starts at the top, and Dr. Kenneth Cooper and his vision served as the role model. The "missionaries" who came to work at the Cooper Aerobics Center shared in his vision and were a very unique group of professionals. The Cooper Aerobics Center initiatives and programs were leader-driven, not so much by individual leaders as by

1

a team of leaders with many common traits. Examples of those shared qualities included a commitment to the "mission" that was constantly being expanded with varied program initiatives, a disciplined approach to the work, the willingness to subsume personal and professional goals to the organizational aims, and an energy level to go the "extra mile" to do what was necessary to achieve results. Upon reflection, perhaps the most noticeable trait was carrying on the work in a positive teamwork mode. All organizations have internal issues, both petty and important, and the Cooper Aerobics Center was no different in that respect; however, because of the nature of the staff and with Dr. Cooper's leadership, they were reasonably nullified and never interfered with the work mission.

As part of this historical background or foundation, key individuals in the field who provided leadership will be recognized, and in reviewing the various aspects of the Cooper Aerobics Center "missionary" activities, those staff who made significant contributions will be acknowledged throughout this book.

CHAPTER 1

Background on the Physical Fitness Movement

To set the stage for the story of the Cooper Aerobics Center as a "mission" for actively changing physical activity and fitness lifestyles, it's important to appreciate that this did not emerge out of the blue. The initiatives from the Cooper Aerobics Center represent but a major step in the long march over time of recognizing the need for physical fitness and its relationship to health and well-being. Consequently, to have a better understanding of the nature of the Cooper Aerobics Center mission and missionaries, a brief jog down memory lane is required.

The "physical fitness" movement has a long history of differing definitions and different focuses over time, but all had a certain commonality. Therefore, to begin with, physical fitness will be defined as it is accepted today:

Physical fitness is the condition of the body that enables an individual to use his/her body in activities requiring strength, muscular endurance, cardiovascular endurance, flexibility, agility, power, balance, and speed without undue fatigue and exhaustion. It is a state of health and well-being that enables the individual to meet all the physical demands of daily living with reserve energy for leisure time and emergency pursuits.

Some health professionals have incorporated other lifestyle habit areas such as nutrition and relaxation into that definition, especially within the concept of wellness. However, for our purposes the focus is on physical activity, or "using the body." That's not to diminish the importance of total wellness, but it is to highlight the core message from our "missionary" perspective: the need to move.

The notion of the importance of and need for an active physical lifestyle through exercise is not a new phenomenon. The ancient Greeks valued exercise and, as we all know, created the Olympic Games. Exercise training was and is a critical factor for soldiers and military preparedness across thousands of years. In the nineteenth century, the notion of a "cult of physical culture" emerged, especially in Western Europe, that served as a springboard for the physical fitness movement in the twentieth century. For example, in Germany, prototype exercise clubs and/or gymnasiums called turnvereins (gymnastic unions) were established, which were brought to the US by German immigrants and Americanized into "Turner Clubs." Some are still in existence today. In the United States, President Theodore Roosevelt preached the need for "the strenuous life" and modeled for his entire life a physically active and vibrant lifestyle. In that respect, he was the first high-profile fitness promoter.

The twentieth century saw the development and expansion of the concepts of physical fitness and physical education as being important areas in the growth of having well-rounded youth in our schools but also as elements of health throughout one's life span. Physical education and related fields such as exercise physiology and kinesiology became accepted as valid scientific and teaching disciplines. There were many key individuals, events, and initiatives that moved the concept of physical fitness and the need for exercise forward. There are numerous examples to be noted that relate to the foundational work that provided the base for when the Cooper Aerobics Center took up the challenge in the latter half of the century to take the "movement" to another level.

In both Europe and the United States, there were serious research efforts to understand the effects of exercise on the body and how it responds to that exercise. Principles were defined for how exercise regimens can affect a multitude of body systems such as the muscles, lungs, and all elements of the cardiovascular system (heart, vascular, and blood components). Pioneer researchers such as Dr. Per-Olof Åstrand in Sweden, Dr. Bruno Balke in Germany (later at the University of Wisconsin), and, in the United States, Dr. D. B. Dill at the Harvard Fatigue Laboratory and Springfield College faculty members Dr. Arthur Steinhaus, Dr. Peter Karpovich, and Dr. T. K. Cureton (later at the University of Illinois) initiated many of those efforts. There were many more pioneers way too numerous to mention whose shoulders future advocates of the need for a physically active lifestyle stood on.

For much of that century, the emphasis was on exercise's effects on human performance. The term physical fitness became popular, and Ed Fleishman's research validated and defined the major components of that fitness such as strength, cardiovascular endurance (called stamina in those days), flexibility, etc. Training studies on the development of physical fitness were able to define the necessary conditions to produce the training effect. Much of the application of that knowledge was toward athletic performance that required high levels of those fitness areas. The original advocates for being active and fit were recognized athletes of the day: Paavo Nurmi, Jesse Owens, and Bob Richards. While the awareness of physical fitness was being established, it wasn't yet translated to the masses to embrace exercise as a daily habit.

The New Perspective: The Problems of a Sedentary Life

The first half of the twentieth century saw massive industrialization and mechanization of Americans' lifestyles. Prior to that just about everyone was physically active out of necessity. One had to walk or ride a horse about everywhere and especially for occupations such as farming, so most people lived a strenuous life naturally. While diseases such as heart disease and stroke were always a possibility, high levels of physically active habits helped to keep the negative effects of high-fat, high-caloric, and high-sodium diets and smoking at bay. Infectious diseases were the primary causes of death and were the primary health concern. Youth were naturally active with play and "daily chore" activities, especially for a predominantly rural population at the time. There was, at one level, no need for structured exercise activity. Everyone got their healthy allotment of movement and activity in the course of daily activities.

The lowering of the need to be physically active on a daily basis resulted, for many, in the development of a sedentary lifestyle. Without a corresponding change to other lifestyle habits like smoking and diet, the incidence of diseases such as heart disease was seen to be on the increase. The advent of World War II and the finding that 25 percent of draftees were rejected for poor health and fitness brought further attention to the issue and a new perspective on the need for physical fitness and exercise. Likewise, autopsies of young soldiers killed in action showed that many had advanced cardiovascular disease at an early age.

President Eisenhower's heart attack in 1955 renewed the interest in the links between a health condition (heart disease in this case) and lifestyle. His physician, Dr. Paul Dudley White, a renowned heart specialist, started a dialogue on lifestyle and disease prevention. That awareness culminated in President Eisenhower establishing the President's Council on Youth Fitness in 1958. It was a national initiative to promote the need for physical activity and fitness, especially for our nation's youth. At that time, our youth were embracing the new sedentary leisure pursuits, such as passively watching television for hours and numerous conveniences that minimized the need to move. The current concern over youth obesity is not new; it was starting to be seen as an emerging problem back then. President Kennedy in the 1960s expanded that council and its mission with a new name, President's Council on Physical Fitness, to promote habitual exercise for all Americans, not just youth, and not just for performance purposes but for health reasons.

These experiences and findings led to an increased awareness of the concept of "hypokinetic disease," a term coined by Dr. Hans Kraus, a noted Austrian physician, physiotherapist, and mountaineer, that suggested many diseases could be caused by inactivity and the sedentary lifestyle. Pioneering longitudinal research by Dr. Jeremy Morris done with London busmen and by Dr. Ralph Paffenbarger on longshoremen and Harvard alumni demonstrated that a long-term inactive lifestyle contributed to premature death and chronic disease, while an active lifestyle helped to prevent them.

There was recognition that heart disease, stroke, diabetes, certain cancers, and conditions such as obesity and lower back pain had many hypokinetic origins. It was slowly being accepted that individuals now had to go out of their way to get sufficient exercise and physical activity to be healthy. The normal daily physical activities demanded by our modern convenience culture were not enough and, in fact, produced a dangerous, sedentary approach to daily living.

Expanded Structured Exercise Opportunities

While sports and athletics had been in high schools and higher education for years, they offered participation for relatively few of our youth. The 1940s and 1950s, however, did see the emergence of nonschool youth sports with such organizations as Pop Warner Football and Little League, which expanded sports participation opportunities and continue to grow to this day.

In terms of adult participation in structured exercise, especially in gymnasiums or exercise/health fitness centers, private "health clubs" were becoming numerous in the 1940s and '50s, appealing mostly to adult weight lifters and bodybuilders, two sports which started to become popular in the nineteenth century. The major promoter of adult exercise and exercise facility provider was the YMCA. The YMCA deserves

7

considerable credit for moving the physical fitness and active lifestyle movement forward. Since the YMCA's inception in 1844 in Great Britain, the physical component of the "integrated spirit, mind, and body" (the YMCA motto) was front and center. Previously mentioned Springfield College was established specifically to educate YMCA leaders. Many famous fitness pioneers were affiliated with that institution over the years, and in many respects, the YMCA was considered a "nursery" for the fitness movement. James Naismith created basketball and William Morgan invented volleyball while there in the late 1800s. The previously mentioned Springfield researchers broke new ground. The national YMCA also established the YMCA of the Rockies in Estes Park, Colorado in the early twentieth century with the express purpose of being an in-service training institution for YMCA physical directors.

The YMCA exercise facilities and leader-led exercise classes for members kept the fires burning for adult exercise activity. Dr. T. K. Cureton was instrumental in defining YMCA fitness assessment protocols and exercise classes in the 1940s, '50s, and '60s that were applied throughout the YMCAs across the country. However, as a member-based organization predominantly in large cities, its impact on the general population could only go so far.

Past the midcentury mark, physical fitness was being accepted as a valuable factor for one's health and physical performance. Opportunities for youth and adult exercise had greatly expanded, especially for sport and athletic endeavors. Government and educational promotion of the need for exercise had expanded. Jack LaLanne, Debbie Drake, and similar "fitness" celebrities emerged with TV exercise shows that encouraged exercise. However, for all that improvement, expansion, and acceptance, the majority of Americans were not engaging in daily exercise. A Gallup poll in 1961 indicated that less than 24 percent of Americans said they got enough exercise. The population at large didn't yet "get it."

The arrival on the scene in the 1960s and '70s of Dr. Kenneth Cooper and his aerobic exercise system became a game changer for the physical fitness movement. This visionary built upon these foundations to

establish a mission—a place called the Cooper Aerobics Center—and
a missionary outreach effort that would get the masses moving. This
we will explore in depth.

35 Aerobic Points

CHAPTER 2

The Cooper Revolution

Dr. Kenneth Cooper established the Cooper Aerobics Center in 1970 to serve many aims and purposes that could be viewed as missionary in function. He had already established himself as an expert in the related fields of preventive medicine and physical fitness and had earned the title the "Father of Aerobics" after doing pioneering work in the 1960s while in the US Air Force (USAF). The story of his initial research efforts and the resulting impact of his work on developing the concept of aerobic exercise and the aerobics point exercise system provides the background for his vision for the future Cooper Aerobics Center and its many outreach activities.

The Development of the "Aerobics" Concept

With the advent of the space program in the 1960s and the development of supersonic jets, the USAF needed to determine the levels of stress and physical endurance that pilots and astronauts could tolerate under extreme environmental conditions. Dr. Cooper, as a USAF doctor, was initially charged with conducting research to determine the effects of exercise on the human body as part of that research effort. As a continuation of that work, he was further tasked with defining a new and more effective USAF physical fitness program for all its servicemen and servicewomen. The USAF set up a state-of-the-art exercise physiology lab for the research, and many studies were undertaken over the course of several years.

There is a generic process in the course of any scientific pursuit of discovery that consists of three main phases: understanding, prediction, and control. Understanding involves investigating the nature of something and how to measure it. If the understanding reaches a certain level of knowledge, then we should be able to predict its effects. Finally, if we know enough about it that we can predict its effects, then we can investigate methods to be able to control it or modify it for a specific purpose. At one level, that model process was followed by Dr. Cooper and the USAF team.

At the understanding level, one of the first questions asked was what was the key factor for physical performance, especially under exhausting and endurance conditions. The answer was "oxygen," and the body's ability to distribute and utilize oxygen determined the ability to sustain exercise over time. The body has two basic pathways to create the energy necessary for the working muscles to keep moving. The first source is the use of the anaerobic (meaning without oxygen) metabolic system. Oxygen is not necessity to generate fuel primarily from the glucose in the blood and glycogen stored in muscle tissue. However, it is not an efficient system, there is only a short supply of such fuel, and one cannot sustain activity for very long anaerobically. The other pathway is called the aerobic (meaning with oxygen) system. In this system not only glucose and glycogen but also free fatty acids in the blood stream can be combined with oxygen for a much larger supply of fuel to sustain movement for endurance activities.

The next question to ask was how to best measure the ability to distribute that oxygen. Working with Dr. Bruno Balke, Dr. Cooper's team utilized the maximum treadmill stress test to measure an individual's aerobic capacity (also called aerobic power, maximum oxygen uptake, cardiovascular endurance, or stamina). It is the maximum amount of oxygen one can utilize. The more oxygen one can use, the longer he or she can sustain exercise with less fatigue. In practical and functional terms, it defined what many would call physical fitness.

Measuring one's aerobic capacity requires assessing the expired air after a maximal effort on the treadmill and is recorded in milliliters of oxygen per kilogram of weight per minute. Extensive apparatus is required to get that measurement. It was found that just measuring the total time on a maximal treadmill test correlated very well with that clinical measure and, as a consequence, actual aerobic capacity does not have to be directly measured. That more economical and practical clinical test would later become a staple of Dr. Cooper's comprehensive preventive medical examination.

If oxygen is the key factor, then the next question to ask was what kinds of exercise would predict an increase in one's ability to utilize oxygen. Many studies over the years had generally shown that duration of exercise over a sustained period of time (such as twenty minutes), with intensity (50–80 percent of one's maximum aerobic capacity or 65–95 percent of maximum heart rate), and with a frequency of three to seven days a week, using a mode of activity that requires large muscle involvement such as running, swimming, etc., would increase one's ability to distribute oxygen. While those serve as general guidelines, a more practical means of quantifying exercise was needed that could be easily applied across the entire USAF.

The Challenge of Going from the Aerobics Concept to "Aerobic Points"

With a basic understanding of the nature and importance of oxygen for sustaining physical activity and knowing the basic training factors that can predict the increase in that oxygen utilization capability, Dr. Cooper's team moved to the next step in the process: the control phase of the scientific discovery process. In that perspective, the issue was that of defining an exercise training system that "controlled" the oxygen demands of a particular exercise effort to produce the changes to modify the subject's fitness level (oxygen utilization capacity).

The challenge was to formulate a system that was user friendly, could be applied anywhere in the world with a simpler assessment measuring process, and had an easy way to monitor performance. The research led to the notion of the "aerobic point" as a generic indicator of effort requiring oxygen that allowed all kinds of physical exercises and activities to be quantified based on how much oxygen was required.

As more data was obtained, it became necessary to design a field test that could provide the same estimate of one's aerobic capacity, could be done anywhere, and could be self-administered without any apparatus. It was found that the distance one can run in twelve minutes also correlated well with one's aerobic capacity, and that test became the first field test for the USAF. Later on, another field test—the 1.5-mile run—was validated and became the field test because it was easier to administer and to this day is used in many field-testing settings beyond the USAF application.

Studies were done to measure the "energy cost" of a given physical activity (such as running, walking, swimming, etc.). Energy cost is the term applied to measuring the amount of oxygen necessary to be utilized to perform a particular physical activity for a certain duration and intensity. An aerobic point was assigned for every seven milliliters of oxygen that was required for a particular exercise effort. Therefore, if a specific exercise effort utilized twenty-one milliliters of oxygen to do that activity, then it would be worth three aerobic points.

Once the point levels could be established for a given effort for a given activity, the next step was to determine how many total points (total exercise) were required to produce the training effect where physiological changes could be seen. What were those changes? First, was performance improved, as measured by treadmill time or the twelve-minute or 1.5-mile run field tests? The USAF data showed a consistent trend that the more aerobic points earned per week, the better the performance on those tests. Dr. Cooper then started looking at more clinical measures and found that with a proper number of aerobic points (reflecting the frequency, duration, and intensity effort definitions), many cardiovascular changes occurred, such as lowered heart rate, lowered blood pressure, increased red blood cells, increased blood volume, and an increased ability of the muscle cells to use oxygen. All these changes are the adaptations the body makes to meet the increased oxygen demands of having to do aerobic exercise.

That proper amount of aerobic exercise was called the "threshold level" of minimum points that would produce the training effect. This brought in the frequency dimension. It was found that if a total of thirty to thirty-five points could be earned in a week spaced out over a minimum of three days (roughly ten aerobics points worth of energy in a day's workout), the training effects would occur. It appeared to be a necessary amount for the changes to occur.

USAF Results and Impacts

The advantage of this system was that the mode of exercise activity didn't matter. Running, basketball, swimming, cycling, etc. could be compared by the amount of oxygen (as defined by the aerobic points) necessary for a certain duration and intensity (pace, distance, etc.). The practicality of this system was that there could be a diversity of combinations (days, points per day, types of exercises) that made it convenient for the individual to get the necessary exercise. That convenience and equivalence of effect helps to motivate the subject to stick with his or her exercise plan. Dr. Cooper's data confirmed this.

As the aerobic point fitness program was implemented in the USAF and large numbers of personnel were tested, the trends were very clear. More airmen and airwomen were exercising on a regular basis, fitness levels improved, and the obese and overweight lost weight. From a medical perspective, clinical measures were showing reductions in blood pressure, blood cholesterol, and the incidence of type 2 diabetes. These research results solidified in Dr. Cooper what he always believed: that exercise can be a form of medicine—more specifically, preventive medicine. The implications for the general public were huge.

Taking Aerobics to the World

During the 1960s, the results of Dr. Cooper's aerobics concept and point system were getting publicized. In 1968, he published his first book, *Aerobics*, outlining what has been presented above and the details of following the aerobic point program. The next several years saw additional books and reports noting the value of aerobic exercise. The general public took note, leading to the jogging boom. YMCAs, schools, and other exercise- and fitness-related organizations promoted aerobic exercise. General Richard Bohannon, the surgeon general of the USAF while Dr. Cooper was serving, was a strong supporter of his work and helped to create the National Jogging Association to motivate all to start exercising by jogging. While the jogger was the popular image, people were engaging in all kinds of physical activities. Fun runs and swim meets for adults and the young expanded.

Aerobic exercise became a worldwide phenomenon. In the country of Brazil, for example, the term for aerobic points was a "Cooper." So instead of asking how many points one got in an exercise session, the question was How many Coopers did you get? In many respects, the physical fitness boom was launched. While many others in the physical fitness and preventive medicine fields made significant contributions to documenting the validity of aerobic exercise, in the broader context, Dr. Cooper's aerobics concept and exercise program served as a needed catalyst for the entire physical fitness and health promotion movement. With a credible research base, it served as a new foundation to get people moving. The bottom line was noted by a Gallup poll in 1960, which indicated that only 24 percent of Americans said they exercised. By 1970 that figure had risen to 50 percent. The aerobics concept and exercise system pioneered by Dr. Cooper was a major factor in facilitating that behavior change.

The Challenge of Leaving the USAF

Following the success of the aerobic point program and the research documenting its health benefits, Dr. Cooper encouraged the USAF to adopt a more preventive medicine approach to their medical services.

The USAF, however, was committed to the traditional disease model for medical practice and would not support any expansion of his initiatives. As a consequence, Dr. Cooper was faced with a decision.

His USAF experience gave him a vision for a comprehensive model of preventive medicine services with exercise as a key component of helping patients' well-being. Likewise, he held the solid belief that exercise is medicine and that physical activity and consequent fitness needed to be researched and applied on a large scale. He recognized that fulfilling the dream of operationalizing and expanding that model required leaving the USAF and striking out on his own. That would entail establishing a self-sustaining preventive medicine health and fitness research and application organization that would become the Cooper Aerobics Center.

CHAPTER 3

Development of the Cooper Aerobics Center

The Cooper Aerobics Center in Dallas, Texas was the culmination of Dr. Cooper's vision that emerged from his pioneering work in the USAF in the 1960s. Upon leaving the USAF, he came to Dallas, Texas, in 1970 to pursue his dream of a model preventive medicine practice and physical fitness center.

Initial Challenges

In many respects, he had to swim upstream against the traditional medical views at the time. First was the view that a physician could not sustain a practice based on just preventive medicine—that is, services to keep someone without disease healthy. Second was the prevailing view about stress testing: that the test in itself was dangerous, especially for someone with cardiovascular disease. Even though Dr. Cooper had demonstrated in the USAF that with proper procedures, stress testing could be safe, that view still was prevalent. Finally was the view that while exercise was of value, aerobic exercise could be dangerous, especially for older adults. Many in the medical community viewed his approach as too risky and dangerous, and he was not immediately accepted within the Dallas medical community. The traditional disease model of medicine was the accepted view.

However, Dr. Cooper was helped by many supporters, such as Dr. Milford Rouse, past president of the AMA, who advocated that the concept that Dr. Cooper wanted to develop would be good for Dallas and aided in establishing relationships with the Dallas medical community. Another key supporter and mentor was Dr. Richard Bohannon, who had been the Air Force surgeon general while Dr. Cooper was doing his preliminary work. As with his effort in Dallas, Dr. Cooper also had his critics while in the USAF. The then Lieutenant General Bohannon was able to deflect the criticism, and, when Dr. Cooper was considering locating in Dallas, was instrumental in helping him get established there. Dr. Bohannon was a Dallas native; went to SMU, which was located there; and retired in Dallas upon leaving the USAF. Over the years, he served in many capacities at the Cooper Aerobics Center and especially within the Cooper Institute. In many respects, Dr. Bohannon was viewed by all who worked at the Cooper Aerobics Center as the "godfather" of the center.

With the support of the above and in spite of the many barriers, Dr. Cooper opened the Cooper Clinic in 1971 in the basement of a bank building with one treadmill and started seeing patients. His practice was slow at first, but once his reputation for providing a quality preventive medical examination was made known and no patients suffered any injury or incidents from the stress testing, his practice grew. It became clear very quickly that more room was a necessity. In addition, there was the challenge to expand into a more broad-based comprehensive health center that included an exercise facility.

With the help of the Tyler Corporation, Dr. Cooper was able to secure twenty-two acres of what was known as the Nichols estate in North Dallas. He was literally off and running. His vision was multifaceted and culminated in the establishment of the Aerobics Center (now called the Cooper Aerobics Center) when it came into being in 1972. Originally, it consisted of three entities: the Cooper Clinic, the Aerobics Activity Center (now called the Cooper Fitness Center), and the Institute for Aerobics Research (now called the Cooper Institute). A brief summary of the history of each entity and its current status will provide a backdrop for the concept of the Cooper Aerobics Center as a physical place—a "mission." In turn, as the Cooper Institute is explored in later chapters, its role in providing missionary outreach services beyond the physical facility will be detailed in depth.

Cooper Clinic

The aim of the clinic is to provide a comprehensive preventive medical examination. Board-certified physicians provide patients with an individualized, in-depth picture of their health and an action plan (with exercise and nutrition prescriptions) to improve it and their test results—all in less than a day. A key component of that exam is the maximum treadmill stress test, which not only provides an in-depth look at heart function but also serves as a clinical measure of one's physical fitness (cardiorespiratory endurance). Over the years additional services have been added, and the Cooper Clinic now offers breast health, cardiology, preventive and cosmetic dermatology, 24-7 direct medicine, gastroenterology, imaging, and a broad range of nutrition services.

As with all elements of the Cooper Aerobics Center, the key factor has always been the staff that Dr. Cooper was able to recruit. Several noteworthy contributions need mentioning. Dr. Larry Gibbons was instrumental in the clinic, maintaining the highest standards of clinical care and designing a comprehensive coronary risk profile analysis. Georgia Kostas, RD, pioneered nutritional counseling and dietary analysis for patients. Dr. Richard Constant served as the resident cardiologist for years and helped to prove that stress testing could be safe and beneficial even for those with disease and initiated cardiac rehabilitation exercise classes. Jane Councilor headed up the clinic accounting record-keeping function for many years, which enabled a repository of well-documented data to be archived and evaluated by the Cooper Institute. Finally, Harriet Guthrie and Cynthia Krug, Dr. Cooper's personal secretaries, played a vital role in keeping his many speaking engagements and patient contacts well organized.

In summary, the Cooper Clinic pioneered state-of-the-art preventive medicine services based on Dr. Cooper's firm belief that practicing an active lifestyle is the best medicine for total health and well-being. Since its inception, the Cooper Clinic has been a partner in good health for more than 105,000 people and has conducted more than 275,000 physical exams by the preventive health-care team.

Aerobics Activity Center: Cooper Fitness Center

The Aerobics Activity Center opened in 1972 with the aim of helping the public achieve the recommended aerobics points and physical exercise for health. In 1981, a fire sparked overnight and destroyed the original building. The Coopers rebuilt the facility in 1982, opening what is today known as the Cooper Fitness Center.

Facility

The Cooper Fitness Center today offers more than fifty thousand square feet of indoor amenities plus thirty acres of outdoor grounds—unique from any other environment in the Dallas area. Approximately two thousand members have full access to both, including:

- Outdoor one-mile, lighted, rubberized track with quarter-mile and half-mile turnoffs

- Three-lane banked-curve indoor track

- Two heated twenty-five-yard, six-lane pools (five feet deep)

- Cardio equipment with consoles, including AMTs (Adaptive Motion Trainers), treadmills, ellipticals, and stationary bicycles (upright and recumbent)

- Technogym and Cybex strength-training equipment

- Power Plate vibration training equipment

- Rowers

- Basketball court

- Indoor cycling

- Exercise classes, including:

  - Mind/body studio for yoga and mat Pilates classes

  - Private Pilates studio

  - Boxing and martial arts studio

- Personal trainer staff

- Four lighted tennis courts with Plexipave surface

- Locker rooms with free day-use lockers, towels and toiletries, private showers, sauna, steam room, and whirlpool

- Laundry and shoe-shine services

In years past, the Cooper Fitness Center also had four handball/racquetball indoor courts when those sports were popular, and as interest waned in those activities, they were converted into group exercise rooms.

The Coop

The Coop retail store sells specialty boutique wear for women, active-wear for men and women, and fitness gear and sports accessories, plus the full line of Cooper Complete nutritional supplements. The Coop is open to members and the public.

Cooper Spa

Cooper Spa's peaceful environment is steps away from the hustle and bustle of the gym—and daily life. Led by licensed and experienced technicians, the full-service day spa offers manicures/pedicures, skin care, massage, body treatments, cosmetic services, "Fit for Him" individual exercise program packages, and more. Cooper Spa's retail boutique is home to the "Beautiful Fit" signature-label line and offers other exceptional skin-care products for men and women, plus a variety of gift items. Cooper Spa is open to members and the public.

Cedars Woodfire Grill

Healthy workouts and healthy eating go hand in hand. At the Cedars Woodfire Grill, located by the gym, all the food is made fresh daily and made to order—there are no freezers, fryers, or microwaves. It's food that tastes good and is good for you.

Cooper Fitness Center Leadership

Since 1972, the Cooper Fitness Center has emerged as the premier health and fitness exercise facility. From the very beginning, fitness leadership was viewed as the priority, and staff were recruited who had the necessary leadership qualities to motivate people to safely exercise. The membership goals of the center were not the traditional quick turnover of new members but placed an emphasis on keeping existing members—that is, a focus on adherence to maintaining the active lifestyle and, as a consequence, retaining membership. Two key leaders in establishing that kind of atmosphere were Bill Grantham and Amy Jones. They created what was called the Aerobics Center family concept by pioneering a number of activities, including 1) focused group exercise classes for special groups, 2) a variety of special events that recognized members, 3) fun runs and fitness competitions, 4) fitness and exercise awards, 5) individualized exercise prescriptions, and 6) sponsoring an AAU seniors swim team. Amy especially developed innovative aerobic dance and rhythmic programs. The list could go on and on. The bottom line is that a camaraderie among the members was developed that translated to having member waiting lists of over two years that have been maintained since its inception. Over the years, the various Cooper Fitness Center directors such as Tom Siekman, Clayton Allhager, Brent Darden, Brad Wilkins, and Bryan Lennon maintained the quality of services, and membership always remained stable.

The Cooper Institute

Although the Cooper Clinic was the first physical entity developed by Dr. Cooper in 1971, the Institute for Aerobics Research was established the previous year (1970). It has undergone several name changes over the years and is now simply known as the "Cooper Institute." In many respects, the institute served as a continuation of the research he initiated while within the USAF. The nonprofit institute was created to develop a rich repository of health-related data so that the basis of his work was firmly grounded on scientific legitimacy, not "faddism."

While the primary purpose for the establishment of the Cooper Institute was the research function, it also was chartered with an "education" function. That secondary function would be to apply and translate the findings from the research efforts that would eventually crystalize into outreach services that defined the institute's "missionary" efforts. The background here is on the research function, and the education and other outreach services will be explored in the next section, Section II.

Division of Epidemiology

The core of the research efforts has been centered on the data collection and monitoring system to track data on the patients who came to the Cooper Clinic for the preventive medical examination. Dr. Bohannon set up the original data collection systems for what would be known as the Cooper Center Longitudinal Study (CCLS). It is one of the most highly referenced databases on physical fitness and health in the world. Armed with those data, the Cooper Institute has worked to make healthy choices easier through credible research, effective learning programs, and an influential network of partners.

The CCLS allows researchers to evaluate the effect of lifestyle choices on the development of chronic conditions, mortality, health-care costs, and much more. Research from the CCLS has led to discoveries that continue to incentivize people to get active, guide corporate leaders on employee wellness strategies, arm legislators with data needed to enact smart public health policies, and provide a myriad of ways to enhance healthy living.

The directors of epidemiology and their research teams have directed those research efforts over the years. Dr. Steve Blair steered the pioneering research for many years with a support team of Dr. Bill Kohl, Dr. Beth Barlow, and most recently Dr. Steve Farrell. That effort has produced over seven hundred papers published in peer-reviewed journals over the past fifty years. The research from this longitudinal study has shaped the way the world now views exercise and its impact on quality of life and longevity.

Division of Exercise Physiology

When the institute and Cooper Clinic initiated activities, Dr. Cooper wanted to also carry on his research from the USAF on new training regimens and modalities, exercise's effects on the human body and medical conditions, and further analysis on the aerobic point system. As a consequence, an Exercise Physiology Division was created within the institute in 1972 with a testing laboratory, and a number of grants were obtained to do a variety of research studies. The first director, Dr. Michael Pollock, initiated a number of training studies operationalizing the frequency, intensity, and duration of aerobic exercises to produce the training effect. He was followed by a series of directors and staff such as Dr. Peter Raven, Dr. Larry Gettman (who did the initial research on circuit weight training), Dr. Don Hagen, Dr. Jill Upton, Dr.

Neal Gordon, Dr. Tim Church, Dr. Conrad Earnest, Dr. John Duncan (who did pioneering work on how exercise can aid in the control of essential hypertension), and Dennis Flood.

One of the major research projects of the division in the early years was a cooperative study with the International Association of Chiefs of Police (IACP), the Dallas Police Department, and the institute to look at the need for police officer fitness and make recommendations for training programs. The Dallas Police Department's liaison was Dr. Tom Collingwood (the police psychologist/physiologist in the department). He would later be hired to develop the institute's Continuing Education Division and would lead its efforts for working with law enforcement agencies.

The exercise physiology research served as a great complement to the epidemiological data. The longitudinal data demonstrated the benefits of exercise and fitness on health and well-being across a number of dimensions. The physiological data provided the necessary information to define the best ways to get those benefits.

Cooper Institute Management and Leadership

Leadership was always an important element for the Cooper Institute, which had an advisory board consisting of scientific and industry leaders that provided an oversight function. That board provided direction for research funding and, later on, for the various service outreaches that the institute provided. The Scientific Advisory Council of the board had recognized experts such as Dr. Ralph Paffenbarger and Dr. Bill Haskell, who helped the institute maintain a credible research model. Dr. Cooper provided consistent stability as the board chairman.

Dr. Mike Pollock and Dr. Larry Gettman served as executive directors in the 1970s when research was the major function of the Cooper Institute. Dr. Charles Sterling served as the Cooper Institute executive director/CEO for several decades starting in the 1980s and developed an organizational structure and system that greatly enhanced both the research and educational/service outreach efforts. As various institute service divisions were created, he was able to sustain a committed staff that was goal oriented. He established an accountability system that enabled all staff to set and reach their respective goals. Because the Cooper Institute was nonprofit and always had to be financially accountable, his fiscal leadership was a valuable and necessary element for the Cooper Institute to sustain itself for decades.

As part of the Cooper Institute management team, Mr. Mark Donovan, Mr. Gary Hodges, and Jan Samuels deserve mention as being key for managing the many personnel issues and keeping the accounting of expenses and income in check. As with Charles Sterling, they served that function for many decades and helped the various division directors be fiscally aware and accountable.

The Funding Challenge

The institute was and still is dependent upon external sources to fund the research, and it is an ongoing challenge always facing the institute. Funding for the research comes from several sources, including government grants, but also from fundraising events, revenue from the educational and other service programs, and a large portion from private donations. To that end, another member of the management team, the director of development, played a vital role. The director for several decades, Dr. Joel Woodburn, was instrumental in securing ongoing private funding to support the research from a variety of sources. Connie Tyne continued in that role for several years as well.

The most successful fundraiser was Dr. Cooper himself. He made almost weekly speeches around the country and the world and used those opportunities to generate interest in the institute's research. In turn, Joel or Connie would follow up with individuals or organizations that Dr. Cooper had talked to, and they were able to create a large number of sustaining supporters from his personal contacts.

Institute Research Conclusions

As was mentioned, over seven hundred peer-reviewed articles based on institute research have been published. A reasonable question to ask is, What can be concluded from all that data reported in all those articles? The CCLS database consists of over 1.8 million person-years of data from those Cooper Clinic patients who have had repeated examinations over a fifty-year period. That allowed for a wide variety of analyses. Mr. Mike Smith and Ms. Suzan Lewis organized a Computer Services Division that was able to sustain an up-to-date data collection and analysis process necessary for all the research goals.

The core belief and hypothesis that Dr. Cooper had since his USAF days was that one's cardiorespiratory fitness level (CRF) provided some protection from disease and premature death. The measure of CRF used by the Cooper Clinic and Institute was the maximum treadmill stress test time that every patient underwent as part of the clinical examination. The longer the time on the treadmill, the higher the CRF (fitness). A patient's relative fitness was categorized from the 1st to the 100th percentile of performance. The continuum of scores by percentiles were categorized into quintiles (five distinct twenty-percentile units) from very low to very high fitness level.

The majority of institute data analyses focused on the differences between the high and low fitness (CRF) quintiles on a number of health measures, risk of disease, and premature death or on the general trends going from very low to very high fitness. It is impossible to describe all the findings that the institute produced; however, a summary of the key research findings demonstrating the importance of physical fitness (CRF) for health and well-being can be detailed briefly:

- Quality of life: Comparisons between those who have high fitness and those with low fitness on quality-of-life conditions show that the highly fit have significantly less risk of having sleeping difficulties, frequent headaches, chronic muscle pain, depressed sex drive, lower back pain, chronic fatigue, and heartburn.

- Development of physical diseases/conditions: Comparisons between those who have high fitness and those with low fitness on the development of physical diseases/conditions show that the highly fit have significantly less risk of developing hypertension, coronary heart disease, heart failure, stroke, kidney disease colon cancer, lung cancer, osteoporosis, diabetes, metabolic syndrome, and chronic conditions later in life.

- Development of mental conditions: Comparisons between those who have high fitness and those with low fitness on the development of mental conditions show that the highly fit have significantly less risk of having anxiety, depression, poor self-esteem, dementia, Alzheimer's, and cognitive impairment.

- Low fitness as a separate risk factor for premature death: Comparisons between those who have high fitness and those with low fitness on the incidence of premature death indicate that the highly fit are significantly less likely to experience premature death from all causes of death and specific causes such as coronary heart disease and cancer. Those with high fitness live on average three years longer that those with low fitness.

- Fitness level is a more significant risk factor for premature death from all causes, and specifically heart disease, than traditional risk factors: Comparisons between those who have high fitness and those with low fitness on the incidence of premature death show that having low fitness is a more significant risk factor for premature death from all causes of death or heart disease than traditional risk factors of having elevated glucose, blood pressure, cholesterol, BMI, metabolic syndrome, or being a smoker.

- Increasing fitness level positively affects health risk and mortality: Increasing fitness from the lowest quintile to the highest quintile shows that there is a decrease in other health risk factors, a decrease in heart disease mortality, and a decrease in all causes of mortality.

The bottom line from the institute's data to date is that Dr. Cooper's belief and hypothesis that "exercise is medicine" has been scientifically validated.

The Cooper Aerobics Center as a "Mission"

The Cooper Aerobics Center, as described, is first and foremost a place that provides preventive medicine and exercise facilities and programs through the Cooper Clinic and Cooper Fitness Center services. While those original entities, along with the Cooper Institute, have been the core of the center as a "mission," additions have been made over the years. A lodge was built in 1983 to house patients and attendees of educational conferences and wellness programs. That lodge (now called The Cooper Hotel, Conference Center and Spa) is a sixty-one-bed, full-service conference center where various groups can host seminars and educational programs.

It needs to be noted that the entire Cooper Aerobics Center complex could not have functioned so well over the years if it were not for an excellent facilities management team. Mr. Bill Walker and Mr. Gordon Henderson after him need mentioning because during the first thirty years of operations, they established an operational system that enabled the center to function in an efficient and effective manner that allowed Dr. Cooper and all the staff to remain focused on the mission of providing services.

SECTION II:
Creation of a "Missionary" Outreach

The previous section provided the background for Dr. Kenneth Cooper's work in the USAF, the aerobic point exercise system, and the development of his vision of the Cooper Aerobics Center. The concept of the center as a preventive medicine and fitness "mission" was to be enhanced by what could be called "missionary outreaches," or services that were to be provided beyond those which the Cooper Clinic and the Cooper Fitness Center provided to its patients and members. The vehicle for those services was the Cooper Institute (CI).

In the previous chapter, the research efforts of the CI were outlined and reviewed, and as was mentioned, the CI also had an educational "charge." That educational function emerged within the CI as the major source for developing and delivering "missionary" outreach services. At a general level, those services were to translate the research findings into real-world applications that would make a difference in people's lifestyles, exercise habits, and general well-being. This section will explore the multitude and variety of services that defined the Cooper Institute's "missions and missionaries." These efforts will be described in terms of what need they filled, what the aims were, what the challenges and details of the efforts were, how they were implemented, and what the results were. A series of five questions will be answered for each outreach service to help explore what was provided and what the impact was.

CHAPTER 4

Continuing Education: The Initial Vehicle for Missionary Outreach

The first formal "missionary" outreach area was the establishment of a Continuing Education (CE) Division as part of the Cooper Institute, and that division, over the years, served as the driving force for outreach initiatives. As with the previous chapter on the development of the Cooper Aerobics Center, many individuals contributed to the delivery of outreach services, and those that were instrumental, especially in providing innovative direction and efforts to CE, and demonstrated the "missionary" zeal will be highlighted.

Question #1: What Need Was Met, and How Did That Need Become Apparent to Us to Address?

While the initial function of the Cooper Institute (CI) was data collection and analysis, it also had a stated educational mission. Basically, Dr. Cooper's general concept was that new approaches would be developed for existing testing and exercise regimens, etc., that would be evaluated for their effectiveness and practicality and, through educational outreach programs, inform others of these findings. Its first initiative was a three-day seminar titled the Aerobics Workshop delivered through the Cooper Clinic twice a year for a few years. This workshop provided attendees a shortened version of the Cooper Clinic preventive medical examination with stress testing and coronary risk profile analysis. The intent was not only to inform but to encourage participants to become regular clinic patients.

In 1979, Dr. Cooper was ready to expand that needed educational missionary outreach to a full-time service within the Cooper Aerobics Center mix. As part of a new clinic building complex, a 110-seat auditorium was added. Tom Collingwood (who had worked in the past with the CI on its project with the International Association of Chiefs of Police) was hired to be the director of the new division: Continuing Education. His experience in conducting training in both law enforcement and military settings would set the direction for initial course offerings.

Upon Dr. Cooper's initiation of the Continuing Education (CE) Division, the immediate task was to define the educational needs that the division could meet through its services. The term "continuing education" was selected because there was a need for the ongoing education of physicians, fitness leaders, personal trainers, physical educators, and others within the wellness fields to upgrade their skills and methods and keep them abreast of the latest developments that were being created almost daily. That continuing education need was many faceted. First was the already established continuing medical education (CME) that physicians had to have to maintain their specialty certification/license. In this case, the CI was accredited to provide CMEs for family physicians.

Tom had existing working relationships with the President's Council on Physical Fitness and Sports (PCPFS), the American College of Sports Medicine (ACSM), and the International Association of Chiefs of Police (IACP) as their public safety and military fitness consultant. Those organizations had their fingers on the pulse of what was needed. Their input, along with his experience over the years in many settings implementing physical fitness programs, helped him to define what were the most important continuing education training needs for those working in the physical fitness and exercise science fields.

As was previously mentioned, people, programs, and organization are the basic factors that account for any effort's success. While all three factors are important, those organizations had critical insight into our nation's fitness movement and needs, and there was a general consensus that the key element consisted of the people factor and that the core element of that factor was fitness leadership skills.

As a consequence, the most critical training needs could be summarized as providing training on needed fitness leadership skills. The growth of the fitness and jogging movement in the 1960s and '70s saw a multitude of "faddish" leadership practices and exercise programs being applied nationwide and worldwide without scientific validity. Examples were "going for the burn" and exercise leaders "showing off" their physique and prowess at the expense of teaching and monitoring their class. Of more importance was the lack of a skill set by leaders of proper assessment and training exercise prescription methods that could place individuals at risk for injury or worse. Adherence statistics consistently indicated that 50-60% of adults who started an exercise program quit within six months. Research indicated that proper leadership skills could positively push those percentages downward.

Besides the definition of training needs, it also became clear, again based on the experience with the PCPFS, ACSM, and IACP, that there was a tremendous void in fitness leader training courses available across the country. There were a few short-term courses that would be offered periodically by a college or a health club but with little curriculum development or proficiency testing. The YMCA did offer a course for their physical directors, but it was in house and just for their personnel. There was a need for a well-defined curriculum course with a strong research base that offered the hands-on training as well as the cognitive skills necessary to be a fitness leader. The CE Division made it its mission to fill that void.

Question #2: What Was the Aim?

The aim of the Continuing Education Division was to meet the obligations of the CI educational mandate as expressed in its 501(c)(3) document. However, more importantly and at a functional level, it was to serve as the missionary outreach division of the CI. It would do this by providing educational courses at several levels—to be the most up-to-date source of the fitness and preventive medical technology and the Aerobics/ Dr. Cooper's model for health and well-being.

The core "service" would be to provide a basic fitness leader training course to the largest population of potential fitness leader trainees. Such courses were seen as the best opportunity to spread the word and develop a client base for further courses and services. In addition, short courses on timely topics would also be provided that would provide yearly continuing medical education credits. As the outreach arm of the CI, Continuing Education over the years would also emerge to serve as the CI "nursery" for expanded outreach services such as special projects, consulting, wellness programs, and a variety of service programs for specific groups and the like.

Throughout all its existence, the CE Division had to deliver its courses and services with a fiscal responsibility that 1) generated the income to sustain support for all of its operations and services with 2) a net income left over to support the ongoing research mission of the CI. Those fiscal goals were underlying aims for the CE Division.

Question #3: What Did We Do?

A series of initial steps were immediately undertaken to establish the CE Division as a viable entity within the Cooper Institute.

Developing the Core Training Course

With a clearly defined aim to address the training needs of fitness leaders as a primary area of course delivery, the next step was to define the course or courses. Before coming to the CI, Tom had designed and delivered several police fitness instructor courses to train academy personnel to deliver law enforcement fitness programs. Because of that experience, CE was able to immediately organize course offerings.

The foundations of that course curriculum served as the model for the design of the basic fitness leader course that the CI would provide titled the Physical Fitness Specialist (PFS) course. The basic skills taught in the course consisted of an eight-step process for defining an individual fitness program and also for designing a program for a group of individuals. Those eight core areas were as follows:

1. Health screening methods

2. Fitness test assessment methods

3. Goal setting methods

4. Exercise and nutrition prescription approaches

5. Designing starter and safety programming

6. Fitness education

7. Motivation strategies

8. Feedback methods

Besides those eight skill areas, trainees also received instruction on the physical fitness foundations of wellness, health risk, anatomy, and exercise physiology.

A program of instruction (POI) or curriculum was defined with performance objectives, teaching outlines, and an eventual proficiency testing process with a written examination and practical examination measuring the ability to do screening, assessment, and exercise prescription programs. In addition, a course manual was designed for trainees with detailed procedures.

Applying a Training Model as Opposed to an Educational Model

Many like to draw distinctions between education (broad-based cognitive learning on given tropics) and training (focused training on skills and applications with well-defined performance objectives). However, it is quite possible in an appropriately designed training course to equip individuals with the necessary knowledge and skills to implement valid research-based fitness programs. The learning from EMT and Special Forces Medical Technician training had shown that focused training can directly prepare individuals to apply many necessary medical and health procedures without all the background conceptual material. Tom's background in training provided a "road map" for the direction of the division as a missionary outreach. That training model of CE was to serve as the focus for all its course offerings.

The focus would be on training as opposed to generic education. The traditional model for many seminars and courses seen in the field at the time was that of a college educational-type course. An instructor would present his or her topic, then leave for another instructor to do his or her topic, and the participants were on their own to digest the material, learn it, and if a test was given, demonstrate they knew the material. The onus in this model is on the learner.

The training model that was applied was slightly different. That model, seen in police academies and military service schools, had little room for trainee failure because of the public safety and military preparedness consequences of having unfit officers and servicemen and servicewomen. There is more of an onus on the instructor to ensure that trainees master the material and meet the course performance objectives. The instructor does what is necessary to ensure everyone can master the content, which means often going the "extra mile." In addition, whenever possible, the content was hands on, with practicum proficiencies having to be demonstrated.

While the training model was the prevalent model, the benefit of it serving as a continuing education experience was recognized. As a consequence, the CE Division was able to establish a relationship with the University of North Texas to grant three hours of college credit for successfully completing the forty-hour CE courses.

Defining the Target Population: The Initial Challenge to Immediately Generate Courses and Trainees

Creating and starting a new program always has challenges and problems getting off the ground. The first challenge was to explore how to meet the fiscal aims of the program. Dr. Cooper took out a loan to underwrite the first year of the division, and that loan was to be paid back with interest by the end of the year. That was real pressure to "hit the ground running" with course offerings as soon as possible. The solution entailed defining course opportunities ASAP.

Once the core course had been finalized, the next critical step was to define who would be the target populations for the courses. At a general level, anyone working in the fitness field such as health club staff, YMCA staff, physical educators, and the like were the natural targets. However, given the situation whereby it was necessary to offer courses immediately to generate income, a select population was targeted based on Tom's experience and network of law enforcement contacts.

Tom's experience over the years of conducting courses for the International Association of Chiefs of Police, the National Association of State Directors of Law Enforcement Training, the American Society of Law Enforcement Trainers, and the President's Council on Physical Fitness and Sports provided him a national network of police agencies that could be contacted immediately and directly. Public safety agencies have dedicated budgets for in-service training that could provide funding for CI training courses. As a consequence, it was determined

hat initial course promotion efforts would be aimed toward the law
enforcement community. That focus was immediately rewarded, and
courses for many police agencies were initiated within a month of the
establishment of the CE Division. It became clear that the law enforcement course offerings would be the staple to sustain continuing educa-
ion at its initial stages of operation.

Initial Operations and Programs

The same PFS course had two basic iterations. The first, as mentioned,
was a contract course with a law enforcement agency whereby it assigned trainees to a given course. There was a set fee for the course
or up to thirty officers. The second was an open-enrollment course
whereby individuals would sign up for a course for a set tuition per
person. Most of the contract courses were delivered on-site to a given
agency, and the open-enrollment courses were provided at the Cooper
Aerobics Center in Dallas.

The first few years demonstrated the growth of course offerings
of the PFS in both contract and open-enrollment courses. While law
enforcement fitness leader courses were the most numerous, other
organizations such as health club chains contracted for courses as well,
and monthly open enrollment courses were being offered. Specialized
courses to "train the trainer" for the cadre of the US Army's Physical
Fitness School staff were offered in Dallas, at the Soldier Support Center
at Ft. Benjamin Harrison, the Army Medical Center at Ft. Sam Houston,
and overseas bases. While the PFS course was the "backbone" and
primary source of income for continuing education services many other
courses, seminars and workshops were also provided.

Several short term (two-day) courses were also developed covering
timely topics such as the "The Value of Stress Testing". Some advanced
courses for law enforcement and military contract clients were designed
and delivered that focused on the concept of a master fitness trainer/
officer who would, in turn, be able to train his or her staff to be fitness leaders. There were requests for international seminars whereby
a client would bring participants to the Cooper Aerobics Center, or CI

Continuing Education staff would travel overseas to provide the courses Seminars were delivered in Japan, Brazil, Austria, Germany, Canada, Poland, Great Britain, Switzerland, Italy, and Saudi Arabia. Dr. Cooper was a primary speaker in many of these programs along with Cooper Clinic and Fitness Center staff Georgia Kostas and Amy Jones.

Cooperative courses were also delivered with the International Association of Chiefs of Police, the President's Council on Physical Fitness and Sports, and the American College of Sports Medicine (ACSM). CE staff taught in the President's Council Regional Clinic courses. The CE Division was selected to offer the ACSM exercise test technologist and health/fitness instructor certification courses and examinations, with Tom serving as certification director for those courses.

Initial Instructional Staff Expansion

As mentioned earlier, leadership was considered the key factor, and the staffing of courses was of primary importance. At first, the course instructors were Tom and CI staff who had a specific expertise they could teach. However, that was only a temporary approach. The model for instruction was to develop a "cadre" or team of instructors who had the skill set to teach all topics interchangeably. This would give tremendous continuity of teaching and provide maximum staffing flexibility, especially when more than one course may be going on at a given time. This is the model that law enforcement academies and the US military have successfully applied for years.

As the need for a professional cadre increased with the growth of courses, the challenge was to recruit individuals who could serve a cadre function. Not everyone is suited for that role. However, Tom was fortunate and in the first two to three years expanded the staff to two more instructors who fit that instructional mode. First was Roger Reynolds, MA, a former NFL player and coach who had hands-on experience in developing and delivering corporate fitness programs, so he had real-world experience. Second on board was Dr. John Poteet, who came from both a public-school physical education and college kinesiology and coaching background. He was a master teacher, and his expertise provided a quality control for the division's teaching effectiveness. Of note is that both were prior military (as was Tom) and readily adapted to and set the tone for the cadre concept. For many years, these three were the primary instructors, conducting courses and workshops on a nonstop basis across the globe.

The Trainee Motivation Challenge

Once those courses had been delivered for a while, it was discovered that trainee motivation became an issue. Especially for those being delivered at the Cooper Institute, some trainees weren't always motivated to go to or pay attention in class. It was like a week at the Cooper Aerobics Center was an opportunity to hang out in the gym and exercise most of the day. As a consequence, a written and practical test was created for trainees to take, and if they passed, they would be certified as a Cooper Institute "Fitness Specialist." It became very noticeable that after doing that, the participants were motivated to stay in class and pay attention. The "Cooper certification" was not only one of the first professional fitness certifications in the field, but it became the most popular and a great source of revenue.

Staffing and Program Expansion Challenges

As the years progressed and many more courses were offered, the need for more professional instructors grew, and staff additions were made. As with the initial staff expansion, it was necessary to recruit the type of individuals who had the necessary skills, energy, and desire to function with a "missionary" attitude. Tom, Roger, and John as a team recruited and selected many capable instructors. The following instructors spent many years teaching CE courses: Dr. Susan Johnson Sterling, Dr. Steve Farrell, Dr. Joe Priest, Dr. Nita Priest, Karen Hughes, James Patselis, Gina Cortese, Stephanie Espinoza, and Rhonda Carter. Other instructors who joined the CE team over time but with shorter durations included Dr. David Hughes, Mike Trexler, Caroline Williams, and Phil Tyne. In addition, several "adjuncts" such as Tom Tracey, Bill Brewer, and L. J. Weber assisted in delivering workshops and courses.

Several of the instructional staff moved into the director's position over time as Tom assumed other responsibilities within the CI. These newly appointed directors brought in new and creative approaches that kept courses up to date.

An issue that emerged was that of other organizations starting to offer competing fitness certifications and courses. As a consequence, new training programs needed to be defined and the variety of course offerings expanded beyond that of just the PFS. One of the directors who greatly expanded the CE courses was Susan Johnson Sterling. Under her leadership, courses were added for aerobic dance instructors, group exercise leaders, strength coaches, nutritionists, and those working with older adults. As with the PFS, proficiency examinations were attached to each course, and it was possible for an individual trainee to receive a number of specialized certifications to apply valid fitness programming and methodologies. She also expanded the topical scientific seminars and specialized courses using adjunct instructors with unique expertise in areas such as biomechanics, functional fitness, and resistance training. The Institutes' Division of Health Promotion designed a health promotion director (HPD) course that eventually enabled the CE Division to provide that HPD course for several years. Ruth Carpenter, RD, was significant in the endeavor.

Other staff serving as directors, such as Joe Priest, provided innovative program enhancements to upgrade all courses with the latest research from the CI and, as the technology advanced, reconfigured course materials into the digital age. Another director-innovator was Steve Farrell, who made significant contributions in translating the science (from the institute's data) to usable course materials and digital modules. He maintained a scientifically based, user-friendly course manual that was unequaled in the field. All of those directors served to keep the CE Division a state-of-the-art operation. The other element was that they led by example and facilitated an ongoing team approach to the entire CE missionary effort.

The Importance of Contract Courses
The mainstay educational outreach service was the contract courses in that they provided a stable source of income. Initially, the contract courses were with law enforcement organizations, especially federal agencies. Example agencies and their liaison officers who were instrumental in working with CE included the US Secret Service (Mauri Sheer), US Marshals Service (Ellen Rogers), DEA (Woody Johnson), FBI (Al Beccaccio), and US Customs (Carolyn Clark Keelor).

In later years, under the direction of Susan Johnson, Roger was tasked to expand and manage contract courses. Besides the existing law enforcement courses, he expanded course contracts for fire and public safety, first responders, and the Indian Health Service. The major expansion, however, was with the military services. He expanded contract courses to include all branches of military services: Army, Navy, Air Force, Marine Corps and Coast Guard.

The basic PFS certification course was expanded to include the master physical fitness specialist course and a "train-the-trainer model" for specific military clients. Roger and Caroline Williams met with military fitness personnel, administrators, and independent researchers led by Wayne Westcott Ph.D., at Langley Air Force base in Virginia, to develop a new course for military exercise and physical training (PT) instructors. They visited several military posts/bases to view and evaluate the PT and exercise class instructors' skills of delivery. The primary concern that emerged was focused on the safety and proper mechanics of exercise movements. The outcome of that development led to the design of the military exercise leader (MEL) course. This newly created course eventually became a highly requested course by all branches of the military services. Roger, John, Steve Farrell, Karyn Hughes, and Gina Cortese provided most of the instruction and were instrumental in meeting the large demand for that course.

The Traveling Challenge
Contract courses being a mainstay necessitated that trainers take many courses on the road. The travel schedule posed several challenges that

had to be met. First, staff had to pack and hand carry all class supplies to the airport and from the hotel destination to the classroom. Those supplies contained anywhere from five to eight boxes of supplies and manuals, with each box weighing fifty to seventy-five pounds. Roger was able to get the institute to secure a large locker that would theoretically carry all the supplies. It lasted exactly one trip before falling apart. Therefore, it was back to the heavy lifting and carrying. The travel demands provided another important rationale for the instructors being fit.

A second factor was the various time zones encountered. Many times, staff were traveling back-to-back weeks at a time. Roger once traveled nine straight weeks. International travel was by far the most difficult. However, even the travel within the US meant that time zone changes necessitated adjustments to eating, sleeping, and even teaching habits. There would be many times that staff would be conducting three to four contract courses on the road, then return to Dallas and immediately teach a course at home the following week. The travel was intensive, exhausting, and extremely demanding. Again, the personal fitness level of staff allowed them to successfully accomplish this schedule.

Beyond the travel issues was the fact that the staff faced a new class of students every week. As John once said, "We met a new board of directors every Monday morning." Every class expected us to bring our A game, with no exceptions, each and every week, and enough cannot be said about the tremendous commitment that all the CE staff made to maintaining such an intense training schedule and, at the same time, providing quality instruction.

Training Setting Challenges

The road courses were delivered in many different settings that could often present some exciting and frequently challenging experiences. Roger and Steve Farrell were teaching in California when all of a sudden, a loud boom sounded, which was immediately followed by the entire classroom moving side to side. Desks and chairs were sliding around the room. One of the students yelled, "QUAKE!" and everybody ran outside, where the earth was moving and shifting. It lasted about five to ten minutes. Their first earthquake was a very scary affair. The same thing happened a year later when they were teaching the California Highway Patrol in downtown Los Angeles and another quake hit. California was not a favorite training site.

All staff had occasion to conduct courses at higher altitudes. The challenge was that we did not have time to acclimatize while the trainees were already used to exercise at altitude. On one occasion, Tom was conducting a course in Colorado at eleven thousand feet. He was demonstrating some calisthenic exercises and in giving the instructions was huffing and puffing while talking. The class immediately nicknamed him "puffer" as they went through the exercises with little breathing difficulty.

Another "oxygen deficit" experience had to do with smoking. An example occurred while Roger and Steve Farrell were teaching a Native American class in a casino in South Dakota. Smoking was allowed everywhere. They suffered through the week inhaling smoke while ironically teaching how bad smoke is for your health. They had to put towels under their doors to help keep the smoke out, but it didn't work that well. Another example occurred in the early '80s when Dr. Cooper, Tom, and Amy Jones conducted a series of seminars in Japan. Smoking was a popular habit over there at that time, and many of the participants were smokers. The trainees were begging for smoke breaks, which were not granted.

Staff were often amazed at how many trainees who were smokers were also exercisers. Tom was in Deal, England, working with the British Royal Marines and would go on morning runs above the Cliffs of Dover with retired physical training instructors, some in their fifties, sixties, and seventies. Many were smokers, and they would be "puffing away" on cigarettes while running the cliffs. They were a hardy bunch. On the other hand, John was teaching a police fitness leader class in Alabama where there were a few smokers, and they were not exercisers. During the 1.5-mile run, they walked most of the way and held an unlit cigarette in their mouth while saying that their "motor couldn't go any faster." A final smoking experience to relate occurred when a police officer lit up during a lecture. Tom, who was teaching at the time, didn't ask him to put it out but instead asked a question: "You have a choice. Do you want to learn, or do you want to smoke?" The trainee put away the cigarette and paid attention the rest of the course. He notified us a month later that he had quit. In the '70s and through the '80s, it was not uncommon to have class members request smoke breaks. Starting in the '90s and later, we did not have any smokers attending CE courses.

Teamwork was critical, with staff complementing each other's deficits. A good example was when John and Tom had vision difficulties at a class in Palm Beach, Florida. Tom, who was nearsighted, broke his glasses one afternoon, so when answering questions during a lecture, John would say, "Question at two o'clock or at nine o'clock," etc. and tell him if he had the right material and spelling on the blackboard. John, who was farsighted, lost his glasses, so at lunch and dinnertime, Tom would order for him. That got pretty old for John, who complained about Tom's choices.

Course Trainees

We found that 99.9 percent of course participants were highly motivated, especially the law enforcement and military trainees. They brought a disciplined learning style reflective of their respective training and work environments. Many of the training settings had the extremes of cold or heat that required a real physical commitment by trainees to do the course requirements. An example occurred at the FBI Academy in Quantico, Virginia, when Tom, John, and Roger were conducting a course in January. The class went outside to perform the 1.5-mile run in zero-degree weather. The FBI agents stripped down to shorts and T-shirts to do the run, while the three of them had to stand still and record the times for three heats of runners (about an hour). That same dedication by trainees was seen when John and Tom did training for the NYPD in January in New York. The 1.5-mile run was conducted by the East River with considerable wind and again in zero-degree weather. All the NYPD officers stripped down to shorts and T-shirts and enthusiastically did the run with no complaints. On Tom and John's last night in the city, they were given several hundred dollars by those same officers to "go do New York." They gave us NYPD Officer Association cards (Irish Officers Association, Italian Officers Association, etc.) and said, "If you get into trouble and get approached by an officer, look at his name tag and flash the right card."

There were hundreds of individual trainees that could be mentioned, but there is only room for a few of the memorable ones that will be noted. One of the trainees in a class delivered in Arkansas was Joe Falcon, the world record holder at the time for the mile run. Watching him run was like watching beautiful poetry in motion, and his perfect running form was flawless. He took the time to coach his fellow trainees, and he stimulated them to perform personal bests when they did the 1.5-mile run. In Dallas, much excitement throughout the Aerobic Center occurred when a Playboy centerfold playmate (Miss July) attended one of the classes. Many staff at the center brought their copy of this Playboy issue and asked her to autograph it, which she did.

You never knew what would happen in a class or what a trainee would do. An example was when Tom and Roger were delivering a course to the Jack Lalanne European Health Club employees in Pasadena, California, when one of the most embarrassing training moments occurred. Trainees were instructed to come to class with gym shorts on underneath their pants to learn to use skinfold calipers to assess body fat because one of the skinfolds was to be taken on the front thigh. Tom had a male volunteer come to front of the class as a demonstrator. He was wearing blue jeans, and when asked to drop his jeans, he hesitated, then dropped them. He had nothing on. Tom immediately turned red. There was a long silence, and he looked at Tom and said, "Hey, man, it's California."

Strong relationships were forged with trainees. Over the years, there were numerous occasions when the police and military trainees would not let CE staff buy beers, lunch, or dinner. Many, especially those on military bases overseas, would provide tours and such on off-duty times. There were occasions when staff were invited to spend a night's stay and dinner with their families. Mauri Sheer, head of the US Secret

Service fitness program, put it best when he told Tom (after about the tenth course delivered for their agents) what he respected and appreciated about the CE staff. He firmly believed that the CE staff really cared about his guys and admired the way we all treated them with respect. He thought that we would do whatever needed to be done to meet their needs. He had complete confidence and trust in us. That dedication by CE staff to trainees was not unique to the Secret Service but was the norm for how we conducted training and served all of our clients.

Later Operations and Initiatives: The "Nursery" Concept

Many of those groups receiving contract courses also requested additional services from the division, such as program and facility design or direct fitness programs for selected employee groups. As a consequence, CE started providing a wide variety of consulting and program services to clients that eventually broke out into individual divisions within the institute, which will be discussed later as separate "missionary" outreach services. This illustrates the concept that the division, as the first outreach effort within the CI, eventually became a "nursery" to birth other outreach efforts.

An example was when Dr. Cooper built the Cooper Hotel and Conference Center on the grounds of the Cooper Aerobics Center (initially managed by Robert Harris and then by Jimmy Fountain) to not only house course participants but to also provide a comprehensive residential wellness program for those needing a more in-depth behavior-modification lifestyle-change experience. While that wellness program was originally developed under CE, it emerged as its own separate division under the direction of Jim Florence.

Question #4: How Did It Work?

Organization

The Continuing Education Division functioned in a similar fashion to a police training academy. Once in operation, a yearly schedule of both contract and open-enrollment courses was established. There were many dedicated support staff who printed and organized manuals and performed all the bookkeeping functions necessary to keep a well-oiled, internationally recognized training and certification program organized and accountable. Susie McCormick, Mona Fontineau, Bernie Bernstein, James Dooley, Ashley Martin, Julie Reed, Laura Fast, Irene Leverette and many more too numerous to name contributed to that effort for many years. Mike Heath was instrumental in coordinating those efforts as well. Their support was critical to ensure all the instructional staff took care of the details necessary for smooth operations. Each course would have an instructor assigned as coordinator who would ensure that all the necessary manuals, equipment, slides, overheads, etc. were in place and in working order.

Course Promotion
Depending upon the nature of a given open-enrollment course, individual promotional brochures were designed and mailed out to a number of purchased mailing lists aimed at targeted populations. As the credibility and reputation of the CI became known, many of the course participants who enrolled were based on them getting word-of-mouth references from previous course participants.

Contract courses were also promoted by recommendations from previous course clients. Since law enforcement courses were the primary contract courses, especially in the early years, an additional promotional factor for them was the law enforcement network that Tom belonged to, especially the International Association of Chiefs of Police (IACP). The IACP would consistently promote CE courses in their publications and recommend and refer police agencies that contacted them about securing fitness leader courses.

An additional promotional effort was that of CE staff providing lectures and demonstrations at national and international conferences aimed at fitness professionals and at industry trade shows. Examples were presentations at law enforcement association meetings (such as the IACP) and writing articles on the police's need for fitness and the need for trained instructors in several police association magazines and newsletters. Many CE staff presented talks and demonstrations at the annual Athletic Business Conference and Military Fitness Conference. Roger was able to actually conduct courses at those conferences that generated approximately $100,000 a year in revenue.

Instructor Credibility: The Importance of Modeling

The training model required an instructor to fully master the information being taught and to possess a high energy level. In turn, that energy level needed to be modeled. All Continuing Education instructors had to practice what they preached and demonstrate it to the trainees. The rationale was simple: it motivated the trainees and gave us credibility, so trainees were more attentive. This was made known in several ways.

First was the commitment to trainees' learning. That often meant showing up early and staying late to ensure everything necessary for their learning was in place and that trainees were prepared to meet the performance objectives. It required committed instructors. A second aspect was to model the physically fit and active lifestyle. We instructors would do our daily workout at either noon or after class, so all the trainees would see instructors serving as role models. This aided in a number of ways: 1) the trainees would gain respect for the instructors, 2) the trainees would bond with instructors, and 3) it set the stage for future work. An example was a seminar conducted to promote the need for fitness standards and fitness leader training in law enforcement. Tom, who was in his early sixties at the time, purposely worked out after the afternoon session so everybody could see a "senior" doing his thing. There were many trainee observers, and as a result, contracts were obtained from two agencies because they were so impressed with his commitment to exercise.

The success of Continuing Education was directly attributed to the efforts of all the instructional staff. The quality of instruction was of the highest caliber, and much of that was due to John's influence. While Roger and Tom were involved in other institute initiatives, John was the constant and stable force for all the courses. Over the years, he was the "workhorse" (providing the most lectures). Not only did his teaching

50

methods serve as a model, but his mentorship of the staff was invaluable. An example was his preparation routine. He always taught anatomy, and even though he probably had taught it thousands of times, he always reviewed his old notes before giving each lecture. It all paid off in that course evaluations consistently rated John as the best instructor.

Question #5: What Were the Results and Implications?

Over a time period of roughly forty years, an estimated fifteen hundred courses were delivered to approximately fifty thousand individual trainees. Those who received the training went back to their respective organizations (law enforcement, military, health and fitness clubs, schools, worksites, health clinics, etc.) and implemented what they learned. Those CE instructor-trained fitness leaders impacted their organizations to be more productive and supportive in assisting others to be more fit and active. The broader-based impact on their institutions will be discussed in later chapters under the other outreach services delivered through the Cooper Institute.

There is no way of knowing how many people were, in turn, ultimately affected by those trained by the CE, but it is likely to be in the millions. No other organization can come close to the outreach that the CE had. The fitness leaders who were trained went out and impacted individual lifestyles in many different ways that may never be known. It's not unreasonable to conclude that the fitness, the activity levels, and the health and well-being of millions were ultimately changed for the better.

The quality of the CE training was such that the "Cooper certification" was recognized as the gold standard for fitness leadership development. The CE Division received many recognition awards from numerous organizations and associations. A few of those prestigious awards would include the President's Council on Physical Fitness and Sports; the American College of Sports Medicine; the American Alliance for Health, Physical Education, Recreation, and Dance; the International Association of Chiefs of Police; the US Secret Service; the US Marshals

Service; the Drug Enforcement Administration; the IDEA Exercise Association; and the US Army and Air Force.

The implications of these results are very clear. Effective fitness leadership can make a significant difference in helping others toward a healthier and more active lifestyle. That fitness leadership can be trained and expanded exponentially to impact more and more people. The CE Division of the CI led the way toward that aim, and the key element of that was the dedicated, energetic, and professional training staff over the years.

The final point to be made is that the efforts of the CE Division were viewed as a "missionary" outreach effort from Dr. Cooper's vision of the Cooper Aerobics Center. However, as with all missions, they must be funded. In the case of the CE Division, the course fees and contracts had to sustain not only its own operations, but as part of the nonprofit CI, to provide overhead support for the ongoing research. Over the years, especially during the periods of economic recessions, the division has been credited with being the single most significant contributor to the Cooper Institute's fiscal survival.

As a division, the focus of Continuing Education was naturally on the delivery of courses and seminars. However, as mentioned previously, it ultimately became the "nursery" for the development and delivery of many more outreach services. Some remained under the umbrella of Continuing Education, and some evolved into separate divisions. The expanded education "missions" will be explored in the next chapters.

CHAPTER 5

Service Outreach
to Special Populations:
Law Enforcement and Military

As was mentioned in overviewing the Continuing Education "mission," many outreach programs and services emerged out of that that division. Two of the major outreach services were aimed specifically at law enforcement/public safety agencies and the military and were provided directly through the Continuing Education Division. The provision of courses to those groups led to them requesting additional services.

A Unique Credibility Challenge
The law enforcement and military populations are both somewhat closed communities. This is due to the unique responsibilities they have, which places them in harm's way with sometimes life-and-death consequences. In some respects, it is not just a career but a way of life. "Outsiders"

such as an instructor or consultant who are not part of their respective police or military families are not always immediately accepted and have to earn their trust and respect. We recognized this because the three of us (Tom, Roger, and John) had been part of those families in the past. The challenge then was that we needed to establish our "creds" with each group we worked with. It wasn't our academic credentials that were important but those aspects of our past that demonstrated we could understand their world and that we were models of what we were preaching about fitness. It became important especially with our first contact with a law enforcement or military client.

Tom experienced an example of this when he was to give a talk to a group of army leaders. He was the last of a long day of professional academic speakers, and he could see the audience was getting burned out. In introducing his background, he made sure the master of ceremonies mentioned he had served in the elite 82nd Airborne. Four members of the audience stood up and yelled, "Airborne," at which point Tom replied with the standard motto reply, "All the way." He could tell that he was immediately accepted, and they all paid attention to him during his talk.

However, it is also possible that one's "creds" can be outweighed by one's appearance. Tom, John, and Roger were doing a course at the FBI Academy. Tom was on stage in this highly professional environment delivering our very serious opening remarks, and he noticed some snickering in the group of agents. It turned out his sweat suit pants were very uneven—one leg below his shoe, and the other pant leg above his sock. The lesson learned was to always prepare your appearance before going on stage.

Some of these clients, such as the Army, the Department of Energy Nuclear Couriers, the DEA, and others, required staff to undergo background checks to get "top secret" security clearances. That was an additional level of credibility that we were able to demonstrate.

In always being the instructor or consultant for clients, one is quite naturally viewed as the "credible expert." However, there were some occasions whereby staff got a lesson in humility on our expertise. Tom was working with CWO Peter Brown of the British Royal Marines Physical Training Branch in England and was invited by Peter to attend a reunion of retired Royal Marine physical training instructors. Prior to that trip, Tom had been involved in assessing the fitness performance of our troops in the Grenada Island engagement. He mentioned to one of the older retirees that our army found out many soldiers couldn't keep up on some long marches in the tropical heat with heavy rucksacks because of a lack of lower back strength. The retired Royal Marine scoffed and said in a Scottish brogue, "Laddie, you are behind the times—we found that out in Burma in 1942." So much for Tom's expertise.

LAW ENFORCEMENT

The provision of fitness leader courses for law enforcement agencies was an initial service offering of the Continuing Education Division, because of the CE director's experience in law enforcement, especially police training. The delivery of contract courses to various agencies often led to those organizations requesting additional services.

Question #1: What Needs Were Met, and How Did Those Needs Become Apparent to Us to Address?

The initial focus of services for most police agencies was to train what were called "fitness coordinators." These would be incumbent police officers who would perform, as a 5–10 percent collateral duty, the function of fitness leader in their agency. They would perform fitness assessments, lead exercise classes, and design exercise prescriptions for officers. Most agencies used those coordinators for voluntary department programs. As time moved on, several agencies discovered that voluntary participation programs and having fitness coordinators was not enough to reach those officers who really needed fitness programs. The only officers exercising were those who already were working out. Even though leadership is the key factor, there was a realization that program and organizational modifications were also necessary to increase adherence. Agencies that had their coordinators trained by the institute CE started requesting additional services to aid them to increase participation rates in their respective fitness programs.

It was found that the impetus for and the sustaining motivation to implement an agency fitness program was dependent upon many other factors, whether there were trained coordinators or not. While the leadership factor was considered a priority, a well-defined fitness program and organizational structure for the program was also required that could withstand the political and management changes that regularly occur in a law enforcement agency. As a consequence, the CE Division developed a consulting/advising service to assist law enforcement agencies in implementing their fitness programs.

Question #2: What Was the Aim?

The ultimate aim of institute services was to assist an agency to institutionalize a fitness program. It was also our goal to be able to be a full-service organization that could help in a multitude of ways to get their officers fit for duty. These services also enabled the institute to create additional revenue streams based on meeting existing client needs.

The goal that was operationalized was that these services were developed to increase the "physical readiness" of police officers. Readiness was a term that better described what the aim was than "physical fitness." In the world of law enforcement, the day-to-day duties were predominantly sedentary, requiring little physical fitness. However, when a critical incident requiring strenuous physical effort occurred, the officer had to be ready to perform, especially since many of those situations had life-and-death consequences.

Question #3: What Did We Do?

The police consultative services originally grew out of the course delivery effort. Continuing education staff (Tom) would meet with agency representatives, outline a process for evaluating their needs, and make recommendations for their physical readiness program. His experience in managing police fitness programs provided a real-world perspective for that evaluation. For most agencies there was a two-stage focus consisting of the following elements:

I. Program Development

1. Research to document the need for fitness: Surveys were used to define common health and disability levels of officers and their fitness levels.

2. Communication and program planning: A fitness committee representative of officers would be created to provide ongoing input and feedback.

3. Program definition: Based on research and communication, a concept paper would be written with fitness program goals, logic, and justification for the program.

4. Program design: Core elements of the program would be defined, including the following:

    -   Screening

    -   Assessment

    -   Goal setting

    -   Exercise prescription process

    -   Starter programs

    -   Education curriculum

    -   Feedback process

- Reinforcement and motivation programs

5. Evolutionary installation determination: Decisions were made about using fitness tests and standards and the process for applying the program to academy recruit training and incumbents Major steps were as follows:

   - Mandatory assessment and education with voluntary participation

   - Data collection

   - Application of reinforcement strategies

   - Mandatory standards phase-in periods

6. Standards validation: A standards validation process would be defined to create job-related fitness standards for officers. Major elements included:

   - Job task analysis

   - Test validation

   - Test cut point (standards) validation

II. Program Implementation

1. Program operations design: Definition of guidelines for the following elements:

   - A well-defined chain of command for program application was defined.

- Program policy and procedures were put into writing and communicated to all staff.

- Physical readiness (fitness) was incorporated into job descriptions and job performance reviews.

- Policy defined that applied to all ranks of officers.

- Medical screening and clearance procedures were defined.

- Light duty policy was defined.

- Regular fitness assessments and exercise prescription process were scheduled.

- Formal education process (written and face-to-face training) was defined.

- A time period for application of standards was defined.

2. Leadership development: Guidelines for administrative and fitness leader functions:

- Administrative authority was established.

- Coordinator upgrade/certification training and collateral duty procedures were defined.

3. Program evaluation: Guidelines were established for putting a program evaluation system in place. Key elements to assess included the following:

- Participation levels

- Fitness level improvements

- Pass/fail percentages to standards

- Job performance ratings improvement

Not all agencies addressed all the various elements listed above. In some instances, the agency chose to address some of the elements in house with their own staff. Most, however, requested that CE perform the necessary work.

Question #4: How Did It Work?

For most agencies, CE would first be contacted about providing fitness leader courses, and that provision of courses could end up being an ongoing service lasting many years. Once an agency had experience working with CE and learned of our capabilities, they then would contract with CE to provide a specific service (such as conducting a fitness standards validation) or to provide general consulting in program development or implementation. However in some instances a given agency would request a specific nontraining service as its initial contact.

By and large, CE did not have to promote its services. Just as was the case for Continuing Education courses, word-of-mouth referrals from existing clients were the norm for getting new agency service requests. The ongoing relationships between the director of Continuing Education (Tom) and the International Association of Chiefs of Police (IACP) and the President's Council on Physical Fitness and Sports were also invaluable for eliciting law enforcement clients and for establishing CE as the premier national resource for law enforcement fitness. First, he became the primary consultant to both organizations, assisting them in their policy statements and recommendations they would make for improving the fitness of law enforcement officers nationwide. He then developed the IACP's Training Key policy and program recommendations that were distributed to all police agencies in the country. Secondly, the IACP contracted with CE to run their existing police fitness workshops. Thirdly, when a police agency would contact the IACP or President's Council for assistance, they would refer them directly to CE. Because of these contacts, for the first decade or so, the many courses and services were developed and delivered by Tom. However, as he moved on to different positions within the institute, Roger and John continued CE's involvement, especially in the delivery of courses targeted at law enforcement agencies.

A cooperative relationship was also established with the FitForce police fitness program, and collaborative efforts, especially for standards validation services, expanded law enforcement clientele. FitForce and CE staff would jointly conduct validation testing of officers and provide fitness coordinator training. Bob Hoffman and Jay Smith of FitForce were instrumental in the delivery of these joint efforts.

Question #5: What Were the Results and Implications?

Over a forty-year period, CE provided specialized services and courses to the sixteen major federal law enforcement agencies under the Departments of Justice, Treasury, Energy, Interior, and Defense. Many of the law enforcement courses were provided at the FBI Academy and DEA training center in Quantico, Virginia, and the Federal Law Enforcement Training Center in Glynco, Georgia, as well as in Dallas. Those same services were also provided to twenty-two of the fifty state police agencies. Each state has a Peace Officer Standards and Training Council (POST), which sets hiring and training standards for all law enforcement agencies in their respective state. The institute worked with six of those state POSTs in curriculum and standards development that ultimately impacted approximately fifteen hundred local police departments across those states. Likewise, independent of a state POST, specialized services were provided to thirty-six individual municipal police departments nationwide.

As was noted in discussing the impact of the Continuing Education courses, it is impossible to estimate how many police officers were ultimately impacted by the institute's services. However, it would not be an exaggeration to claim that those services impacted most of the eight hundred thousand sworn law enforcement officers in the United States. The Cooper Institute's CE Division changed the face of law enforcement since 1979. Prior to the initiation of CE services to law enforcement, most agencies did not have in-service fitness programs for incumbents and no fitness standards. That has changed due to CE's work in this area. While most police academies had always had physical training (PT) classes, they were not aimed toward teaching recruits how to maintain fitness throughout their career. That changed as well, and physical readiness training is now a core element of most if not all academy training curriculums. The "Cooper tests and norms" are being used across the country by federal, state, and local law enforcement agencies.

SERVICES PROVIDED TO OTHER PUBLIC SAFETY AND SECURITY AGENCIES

Consultative services were also provided for public safety/fire departments. A public safety agency such as the DFW Airport Public Safety Department had its personnel cross-trained as both police officers and firefighters. The major services that CE provided for such departments included program design, standards validation, and in two agencies, the direct delivery of a firefighter fitness program. In addition, CE developed fitness standards for security personnel at several Nuclear Regulatory Agency nuclear plants and NASA's Stennis Space Center.

MILITARY

Because of Dr. Cooper's, Dr. Bohannon's, Tom's, Roger's, and John's backgrounds, there was always an interest in and concern for the fitness and physical readiness status of our military servicemembers. In 1979/80, the Department of Defense (DOD) was recognizing that the physical readiness of our military personnel was not where it needed to be. They contacted the President's Council on Physical Fitness and Sports about putting together conferences and initiatives to upgrade the military services programs. Casey Conrad (the executive director of the council) and Dr. Richard Keelor (the council's director for programs) organized a large DOD conference and asked Tom to speak about the results of the law enforcement fitness coordinator training model. As part of that meeting's breakout sessions, he discussed at length the need for an army fitness leader training program. That conference (implemented in 1980) became the springboard for CE's initiative with our military services.

US ARMY

Prior to that conference, the army in 1979 had a small unit with limited resources based at the Ft. Benning Infantry School that had the responsibility for the army's Physical Readiness program. The President's Council recommended that the leadership of that unit meet with Tom to get input on potential program modifications. As was previously mentioned, Tom had served as a paratrooper with the 82nd Airborne (what many considered to be the most fit unit in the army at that time) and, while serving, led many physical training (PT) sessions. That practical experience, along with his academic and work background, enabled meaningful discussions of potential physical readiness program adjustments that were later factored into CE's advisory/consultant role with the army.

Question #1: What Need Was Met, and How Did That Need Become Apparent to Us?

In follow-up conversations (to the preliminary meeting in 1979 and his conference participation) with army personnel, Tom discussed the need for planning to address people (leadership training), programs, and organizational structures to upgrade the army's Physical Readiness program. He was asked to assist the army in 1) redesigning all the elements of the army's Physical Readiness program and 2) creating a Physical Fitness School to train fitness leaders throughout the army.

Question #2: What Was the Aim?

The aim of CE was threefold. First was to get input to determine what the army had defined as their critical needs to upgrade the people, program, and organizational factors for their Physical Readiness program. Second was to address their stated desire to create a Physical Fitness School, and third was to define what the unique services were that CE could provide that the Army did not have the capability to meet. As veterans, Tom, Roger, and John, saw this army mission outreach as part of the ongoing patriotic duty that they had originally signed up for in entering the military years before.

The army's aim was, simply put, to increase the physical readiness of combat and support troops to be "Fit to Win" and to provide a comprehensive wellness program for personnel and their families to enhance their total well-being.

Question #3: What Did We Do?

Initial Assistance

The first efforts were a series of meetings with representatives of the four army commands that were the major proponents of the Physical Readiness program. There was the US Military Academy at West Point, who wanted the future officer corps to have the most up-to-date physical training and to be able to demonstrate fitness leadership regardless of assignment. There was the Army War College at Carlisle Barracks in Pennsylvania (the army's graduate school for future generals), who had the same basic aims as West Point but also wanted general staff officers to be leading advocates of army fitness initiatives. There was the surgeon general's office, who wanted to ensure the Physical Readiness program was medically sound. Finally, the army had decided to establish a Physical Fitness School at the Soldier Support Center at Ft. Benjamin Harrison, Indiana.

As time moved on, there was a recognition that for physical fitness to be accepted and institutionalized, it was necessary that the army's Training and Doctrine Command (TRADOC) and Personnel Division be incorporated into the planning and implementation discussions. The result of this process highlighted different concerns over the various elements of the program. Major services that Continuing Education provided were as follows:

- Physical Fitness School:

    - Curriculum development input for the master fitness trainer (MFT) military occupational specialty (MOS) with associated curriculum and training program through the Physical Fitness School. These MFTs were responsible for all physical fitness testing and training at the battalion level and below.

    - Provision of a training curriculum to enable the cadre of the Physical Fitness School to brief army commands worldwide.

    - Provision of training courses and presentations to school cadre.

    - Provision of briefings and seminars for army commands in the US, Europe, and Asia.

    - Input on the development of a new, more up-to-date army Physical Readiness field manual, FM 21-20, with individual and unit exercise regimens.

    - Input on the development of family and youth fitness programs and materials.

    - Provision of specialized fitness leader courses for army Criminal Investigation Division (CID) and Military Police. Many of these iterations were based on CE's Police Fitness Instructor course.

- Surgeon General's Office and Office of the Chief of Staff of the Army:

  - Provision of training courses for surgeon general's staff.

  - Recommendations for the army-wide physical fitness tests, norms, and standards.

  - Recommendations for the establishment of army post Health Promotion Centers.

  - Recommendations for medical screening for the physical readiness/fitness program.

  - Recommendations for physical readiness/fitness program delivery so that physical readiness/fitness was institutionalized as a necessary component of army life at the same level as firearms qualification and was integrated within army leadership.

Follow-Up Assistance

Follow-up services provided were to respond to requests for review and input on policies and upgrades being made in the overall physical readiness program and organizational support systems. One major focus was on the Army Physical Fitness Test (APFT) battery, norms, and standards. As the years unfolded and the Physical Fitness School instituted their training programs, CE staff would periodically provide ongoing input to cadre staff. Services varied from input consultation, presentations, seminars, and training.

Question #4: How Did It Work?

The initial focus of the services that CE provided was to consult on the development of the Physical Fitness School. CE staff were tasked with immediately providing briefings to army commands and with the design of the master trainer course. CE staff were sent to Ft. Benjamin Harrison to provide curriculum direction and training. In turn, CE staff (Tom and Roger) were sent with the Fitness School director to various commands worldwide to conduct briefings and seminars. Likewise, Fitness School cadre came to Dallas for training courses. The remaining services that CE provided to the Physical Fitness School, surgeon general's office, or the chief of staff's office were provided as requested. This necessitated CE staff often traveling to Ft. Benjamin Harrison, the Pentagon in Washington, DC, and Ft. Sam Houston (the army's medical training center).

The initial briefings conducted by CE staff were for general and field-grade staff of the various army commands. CE staff were well received, and Tom even got a "late" army promotion for his briefings to the generals of the Third Army Command. Somehow, he started getting correspondence before the briefing date addressed to Dr. Tom Collingwood, colonel retired. He didn't pay any attention to it, and unknown to him, the briefing paper given to the generals contained that salutation. At the end of his briefing, he got a question from one of the generals asking him where he had served. Tom acknowledged that he had only been an enlisted noncommissioned officer (NCO) but greatly appreciated the promotion. There was a long silence, and the entire group laughed and applauded. One general stated that he sure looked and acted like a retired colonel and offered to buy his dinner and drinks at the Officers' Club.

Question #5: What Were the Results and Implications?

Within a year of the redesign of the Physical Readiness program, new and updated programs were instituted army-wide through TRADOC, and master fitness trainers were graduating from the Fitness School (7,500 by 1991) and being assigned army-wide. Fitness curriculums were established at West Point and at the War College, and fitness was integrated into the leadership structure. The year 1982 was named the Year of Physical Fitness for the army to emphasize its importance to the command staff. Administrative policy and procedures were established that institutionalized fitness, such as having to meet a fitness standard to get promoted or to be selected for an army school. The bottom line was the army culture embraced physical fitness, and fitness levels dramatically improved service wide.

Conflicts and wars are the final testing ground for whether a given military policy or program was or is effective. The Gulf War of 1990–91 provided the testing ground for the upgraded physical readiness program. The Army Fitness School as well as TRADOC reviewed after-action reports of how units and soldiers performed during that conflict. In response to that analysis, it was concluded that the troop's fitness levels greatly contributed to their battlefield success. As a follow up, the army's Fitness School's commander sent a letter commending the institute's efforts to CE staff with the following quote:

> In many people's view the success of our troops in Southwest Asia was due in large part to their physical and mental conditioning. It is professionals such as yourself that have earned the Institute its fine reputation. You should feel good knowing that you played a role in getting them "FIT TO WIN." The Army Fitness School is grateful for what you've done for us.

UNITED STATES AIR FORCE (USAF)

Because Dr. Cooper had developed the USAF fitness program (aerobic points and field fitness tests), when the USAF responded to the DOD initiative to upgrade the service's fitness programs, the institute was contacted.

Question #1: What Need Was Met, and How Did That Need Become Apparent to Us?

The USAF initial efforts were under the authority of the Morale, Welfare, and Recreation Command at Randolph Field Air Force Base. The need expressed by USAF personnel was that their fitness program should address broad-based wellness and health promotion at an individual level.

Question #2: What Was the Aim?

The USAF aim at the time was that CE revise and upgrade the existing USAF fitness manual to address a broader-based health promotion and provide an upgraded aerobic point system as the fitness training regimen. The initial perspective of the USAF was that individual airmen and officers were responsible for their own fitness levels and training, so the opinion was that the more comprehensive approach as the army instituted was not required.

The aim of CE was to assist the USAF meeting that aim of a revised USAF fitness manual and to provide recommendations for a broader-based approach to installing fitness programs in the service.

Question #3: What Did we Do?

As requested, CE developed a comprehensive health promotion/wellness manual for individual use. Major sections involved: exercise and fitness, nutrition, stress management, alcohol and drug abuse prevention, and prevention of hypertension and other major risk factors. We also made recommendations for expanding their fitness test from just a 1.5-mile run to include muscular endurance measures and body fat. Jim Florence did most of the writing and produced an outstanding manual.

Question #4: How Did It Work?

After initial meetings to discuss potential program and fitness test expansion, the remaining contacts revolved around the development of the USAF Fitness and Wellness Manual. CE staff would create a section, then forward it to the USAF for review and feedback. Once the final version was approved, CE was tasked to develop a fitness test manual that included muscular endurance tests (sit-ups and push-ups).

Question #5: What Were the Results and Implications?

The USAF approach was considerably different than the army's because it was reflective of a "technical service" with very few personnel (with the exception of pilots) in combat positions. This was a major reason for a focus on individual programs. That aspect of that particular service influenced the fitness program model and approach.

While CE did make recommendations and provided a testing procedure manual for an expanded fitness test, the USAF did not apply that expanded testing. The 1.5-mile run was maintained as the service's only fitness test. The fitness model that they applied was one of each individual taking the yearly fitness test, then using the updated fitness manual to follow a personal program.

In succeeding years, the USAF realized that just having a program and organizational structure for a fitness program was not enough, and they did create a two-week "fitness specialist" course in 1986 at Keesler Air Force base that was modified from the army's three-week master fitness trainer course. It cannot be determined, however, the extent to how successful the USAF approach was in getting airmen and officers fit or their adherence to a fitness program. However, in a Department of Defense (DOD) meeting in 1990 to review the status of programs since the initiation of the military-wide fitness program expansion, the USAF did report considerable improvement in physical readiness among officers and airmen.

FURTHER SERVICES FOR THE MILITARY

The big push for upgraded physical fitness programs for the US military occurred in the 1980s and early 1990s. In succeeding years, while the military maintained their programs, it was not as much of a major training focus. The Afghanistan and Iraq conflicts renewed the interest of the US armed services in the importance of physical fitness, and the CE Division of the Cooper Institute was contacted about providing fitness leaders courses. As was mentioned under the CE Division chapter, Roger modified the basic PFS course content and objectives and greatly expanded course offerings for all the military services (Army, Navy, Marines, Air Force, and Coast Guard). His prior experience serving with the army's Infantry School in leading PT sessions provided a practical background for his efforts in developing and delivering the military courses.

In addition, Tom also provided training and consultative services to some allied foreign military services, including the British Royal Marines (consultation on reinforcement and motivation strategies), Saudi Arabia National Guard (fitness programming) and the Swiss National Guard (fitness assessment testing). Coupled with the many requests for services from our military forces, these relationships reflect the recognition that the CE Division of the Cooper Institute had considerable expertise to assist military forces.

CHAPTER 6

The Aerobic Fitness and Stress Management Program for Teachers

As was previously mentioned, the Division of Continuing Education was the first formal outreach effort of the Cooper Institute and eventually functioned as a "nursery" for other outreach services. While the police and military services were an extension of the CE Division courses, the first example of a separate division being created was the application of a fitness and stress management program for public school teachers.

The implementation of the Dallas Independent School District (DISD) Aerobic Fitness and Stress Management Program included three phases. Phase one consisted of a pilot program, and phase two was the delivery of a DISD district-wide voluntary program. Phase three would be to duplicate this same program in other school districts. That necessitated the creation of a new CI division of Special Projects.

PHASE ONE: DISD PILOT

The Cooper Institute initiated the pilot teacher Fitness and Stress Management Program with the intent that it serve as a model that could be applied on a larger scale.

Question #1: What Need Was Met, and How Did That Need Become Apparent to Us to Address?

In 1981, considerable concern was expressed in the City of Dallas over the health and well-being of public-school teachers in the DISD. Teacher absenteeism, stress, morale, and substance abuse were "hot topics." The Cooper Institute was approached by an influential private citizen about how we could offer a strategy for dealing with these problems.

The director of the Division of Continuing Education (Tom) had applied exercise as a stress management approach in previous settings and along with the executive director, Charles Sterling, met with that concerned private citizen and the DISD superintendent to discuss how a potential fitness program could address teacher stress. This meeting culminated with the private citizen's foundation providing the funding for a pilot program for teachers using exercise to address teacher morale and consequent stress.

Question #2: What Was the Aim?

The aim of this pilot program was to assist teachers in becoming more physically fit and in learning how to combat stress. The problem of teacher stress was being recognized as a critical factor in their performance, and the program was viewed as a potential solution. An additional goal for the institute was to initiate outreach activities, and the Aerobic Fitness and Stress Management Program was an excellent opportunity toward that aim as a cooperative effort between the CI and the DISD. An important aim of phase one was to determine the extent to which a fitness program would have a positive impact on teachers' well-being and stress management.

Question #3: What Did We Do?

The DISD program of Aerobic Fitness and Stress Management was managed by the Cooper Institute's Division of Continuing Education. This pilot also served as a learning vehicle for future CI outreach initiatives.

Program Planning and Design

The CE associate director (Roger) was responsible for designing and delivering the program. He had previous experience in the development and delivery of similar programs in business and industry over the past eleven years. In consultation with CE staff, he designed the pilot program that would include the following elements: pre- and post-program medical screening and physical fitness evaluations, individual counseling, goal setting, development of personal exercise and nutritional programs, classroom module instruction, group exercise sessions, motivational and behavior change strategies, and provision of weekly teacher feedback on all assigned work. He was assisted in these delivery responsibilities by available CI staff, Cooper Fitness Center staff, and subcontracted exercise leaders. Tom was responsible for all administrative details and the director of epidemiology of the CI, Steve Blair, was responsible for developing an evaluation design, data collection, and analysis for the pilot.

School Selection

Three DISD schools were identified as delivery sites for research purposes. These schools were selected in meetings between CI staff and DISD administrative staff. Principals of the selected schools met with Roger and DISD administrators to determine all administrative and delivery issues. Final approval for program design was completed, including all program scheduling. DISD schools selected were Gabe Allen Elementary (located in southwest Dallas), which had a primarily Hispanic student and teacher population; Oliver Wendell Holmes Middle School (located in south Dallas), which had a primarily African American student and teacher population; and W. T. White High School (located in

North Dallas), which had a middle- and upper-class white student and teacher population.

Teacher Briefings

Roger met individually with the selected school principals to discuss how the program information would be delivered to the teachers. It was agreed that he would make a one-hour presentation to teachers at each school explaining all details of the program, outcome objectives, and what the teachers could expect. The presentation was held in the auditorium at each selected school before the school day began. All teachers were told that this program would be delivered by staff from the Cooper Institute and would be completely voluntary. Additional information given to the teachers included that all program components would be delivered on campus and within the school day. There would be no cost to the teachers. Finally, the teachers were reminded that one of the primary outcome objectives of this pilot program would be for the DISD administration to consider this program for the entire district.

A question-and-answer session immediately followed the presentation. Teachers were given the opportunity to choose whether or not they would participate in the program. Within a very short period of time following this presentation, there were more than enough teachers who voluntarily signed up to participate. Thirty teachers from each school were given the opportunity to participate. Following the teacher orientation sessions, each selected school principal, CI staff, and DISD staff met to discuss final program delivery details. A follow-up briefing with each principal and selected teachers in their building was initiated to discuss when the program would begin and openly discuss any last-minute questions.

As the program progressed, the importance of all this preliminary planning must be underscored. A positive relationship was established between the DISD personnel and the CI staff that led to a very smooth cooperative effort.

Program Implementation
The sequence for the program was established for a twelve-week cycle and consisted of the following elements:

- Pre-program assessment and collection of personal health information of participants

- Pre-program health and fitness screening of each participant

- Individual fitness counseling and goal setting

- Development of individual lifestyle exercise plans

- Exercise classes at each school

- Educational modules on health and wellness topics

- Post-program health and fitness assessment of participants

- Final group discussion and feedback session with participants

Question #4: How Did It Work?

Pre-program Assessment and Collection of Personal Health Information of Participants
Teachers were asked to complete a questionnaire related to their previous levels of stress, the influence this stress had on their mental and physical well-being, identification of stress triggers that influenced their day-to-day behavior, where the teachers believed their stress was originating, and their previous stress-management techniques. Similar questionnaires were used to determine the teachers' previous exercise and activity habits. A profile of each teacher's previous perceived level of stress and his or her participation in physical activity was developed.

Pre-program Health and Fitness Screening of Each Participant

These assessments were administered by the program director and CE staff at the school sites. The assessments consisted of the following: body weight, height, resting blood pressure, resting heart rate, body composition, flexibility, upper- and lower-body absolute strength, dynamic strength, and cardiovascular endurance with a treadmill test.

Individual Fitness Counseling

Once the assessments were completed, each teacher received a ninety-minute individual counseling session to interpret the importance and meaning of his or her medical screening and fitness scores. The Cooper Clinic's normative data was used as a comparison to record each teacher's fitness score—i.e., cardiovascular, flexibility, body composition, upper-body absolute strength, and muscular endurance. After receiving this information, Roger met with each teacher individually to develop his or her personal fitness profile. This information included a combination of medical screening scores and fitness test results. This personal profile became the basis for their personal goal-setting session.

The following week consisted of a one-hour educational module on goal setting. During this session, each teacher developed his or her personal goals for each measured fitness component. All teachers were provided a personal workbook/manual to be used throughout the program. This workbook/manual would be completed by the teacher as each specific educational topic was presented. Upon completion of the program, each teacher had a personal workbook that covered all program information.

Development of Individual Lifestyle Exercise Plans

Following the initial development of each teacher's personal workbook, which included his or her lifestyle, medical history, fitness assessments, and goal-setting plans, the next step was for the teachers to organize their personal exercise and nutrition plan. Once the teachers understood this information, they were ready to receive an educational module directly related to each area of fitness. The teachers learned how to properly monitor themselves during exercise and gauge the intensity of their work. Teachers were taught how to use the Rated Perceived Exertion (RPE) chart or the Heart Rate Monitoring System. Finally, teachers were taught how to use the aerobic point system for proper monitoring of their exercise intensity and duration. All teachers gradually attained an average of thirty-five aerobic points per week. Their week's total of aerobic points needed to include a minimum of two different exercise modalities, such as walking and biking or an exercise class and walking, working toward cross-training strategies. Each teacher received a handout from Dr. Cooper's book containing the aerobic point system, which assisted them in calculating their own aerobic points per workout. Teachers could simply report their total number of aerobic points per day and then transfer to the total aerobic points per week. This reporting system allowed the program director to monitor each teacher's weekly exercise progress.

Exercise and Educational Classes

All group exercise sessions were held weekly for the twelve weeks. The group exercise classes were held in each school's gymnasium. The first exercise class was during the second week of the program and was a hands-on class on learning to do correct exercise. In this regard, the teachers were taught proper self-monitoring techniques, proper body mechanics, and the anatomy of an exercise routine, which should include a warm-up period, cardiovascular exercise, functional strength exercise, flexibility exercise, and cooldown period. Each weekly group exercise class was typically fifty minutes in length. The exercise classes were definitely one of the more popular activities, and over 90 percent of the teachers reported enjoying the class on the program evaluation.

Each week, the teachers met in a classroom designated for this program. This one class per week consisted of an educational module followed by group exercise. Typically, the teachers participated in the exercise class during the school dismissal time. However, since participating teachers were dismissed from any after-school responsibilities, they had plenty of time to finish the group exercise class. In fact, the teachers were typically asking for more and more exercise time, and they really enjoyed the group exercise class. All teachers were required to remain in their building until approximately 4:00 p.m. Therefore, they had almost an hour after school to work on their personal schoolwork or whatever they needed to do before leaving the building. It appeared that the time period immediately after school until the evening meal was a very high-risk period for teachers to acquire negative habits, and the exercise classes offered a healthier alternative.

Educational Modules

The program schedule consisted of one day per week for twelve consecutive weeks. The teachers met with Roger during this one-hour class in which he covered the assigned work, reviewed new work assignments, and delivered the assigned class educational module. Each educational module delivered during this weekly session was immediately followed by the group exercise class. The following educational modules included:

- The nature of a physical program

- The concept of wellness and risk

- Nutrition

- Nutrition and exercise

- Aerobics/cardiovascular

- Muscular strength

- Flexibility

- Stress

- Relaxation and stress management

- Alcohol, drugs, and addiction

- Fitness adherence

Post-program Health and Fitness Assessment

The same questionnaires and assessment that participants received at the pre-program testing were provided to them. Pre–post changes were measured, and participants also provided a written evaluation of the program.

Final Group Discussion and Feedback Session with Participants

Following the teachers' post-program assessments and evaluations, reports, etc., an enjoyable and very rewarding follow-up class was provided. The focus was on reviewing and openly discussing the following items: pre–post health and fitness score improvements, personal goals achieved, exercise adherence strategies, thoughts on how exercise had helped participants' personal stress management, whether participants lost weight, whether participants had feelings of improved self-esteem, and whether participants' knowledge of personal health and fitness improved. It was a fulfilling discussion with the teachers, and many reported significant positive improvements. As a final reward, a pizza-and-salad dinner was provided for all participants.

Question #5: What Were the Results?

To assess the program's effect on the teachers, a quasi-experimental design was employed. A total of eighty-nine teachers volunteered at the three schools to receive the program. An additional thirty were recruited to be a control group who did not receive the Fitness and Stress Management program but did receive the pre- and post-program testing so comparisons could be made.

Physical Changes

Pre–post comparisons indicted that the control group did not make any significant changes on measured physical factors. However, significant changes were noted for the eighty-nine receiving the program. They made statistically significant changes on a number of factors, including an 11 percent increase in daily physical activity, a 29 percent increase in upper-body strength, a 4 percent increase in flexibility, a 16 percent reduction in body fat, and a 20 percent increase in cardiorespiratory endurance. Of significance was that only 6 percent of those participating were classified as vigorous exercisers before the program, and after the program, 40 percent were classified as vigorous exercisers.

Psychosocial Changes

Written surveys were administered to assess a number of psychosocial factors, and as with the physical factors, the control group did not demonstrate any changes. Those who participated in the program showed significant increases in their knowledge of physical fitness and health issues, their job satisfaction, their self-concept, and their general feelings of well-being, such as reduced anxiety and depression. One important point is that the sources of teacher stress did not change while they were in the program; however, their ability to handle stress significantly improved.

As was mentioned, this iteration of the Aerobic Fitness and Stress Management Program was viewed as a pilot program for potential future applications. The success of the program on physical and psychosocial factors and the overwhelming positive feedback from participants made a strong case for enlarging the program district-wide within the DISD.

PHASE 2: THE FULL-SCALE, DISD-WIDE PROGRAM

Question #1: What Need Was Met, and How Did That Need Become Apparent to Us?

Following the success of the pilot program, it became clear that the program could meet the need for teachers to better handle the stress of their jobs. Follow-up meetings with Linus Wright, the superintendent of the DISD, secured a commitment to expand the program to be offered to all DISD teachers.

Question #2: What Was the Aim?

The aim was identical to the pilot program—that is, to assist teachers in becoming more physically fit and in learning how to combat stress. In addition, implementing the program district-wide offered an excellent opportunity to demonstrate the value of exercise for an employee group on a large scale. The DISD Aerobic Fitness and Stress Management Program would become a major undertaking within one of the largest school districts in the United States. This program would in fact become history making in the field of employee fitness and wellness.

Question #3: What Did We Do?

Following the success of the DISD pilot program, everything was in place to move forward with a proposed district-wide program that was designed after the pilot program. Statistical data and results from the pilot program were presented to the DISD Board of Education. Following the approval by the board, the program was made available to every teacher in the DISD. After hearing all the details of what this program would include, each teacher was given the opportunity to participate.

Initial Challenges

An initial challenge was to define how to manage and deliver a large-scale program in numerous school settings for thousands of teachers. The answer was immediately seen as designing a team approach to program delivery. The details below will outline how that approach was successfully implemented through planning, staff selection and training, supervision, and assignment.

The experience of the pilot program highlighted another potential challenge in that there can always be a hesitancy for program acceptance ("buy-in") and participation if the provider is an outside organization. In recognizing that, we designed an integrated approach to managing the program. DISD and CI staff (some of whom were also certified teachers) would make joint presentations and discussions with teachers. Planning, promotion, and evaluation were joint ventures. In the end, this joint approach was successful in that the teachers viewed the program as a DISD venture, not a CI one. DISD staff were key.

DISD Administrative Staffing

DISD Superintendent Dr. Linus Wright played a very significant role in the district approving and embracing the program. Dr. Wright became a highly positive role model for the program, and his verbal and physical actions in support of the program were extremely valuable to participating teachers throughout the entire district. DISD was extremely fortunate to have such a positive leader role model to not only lead by his verbal support but by his personal example.

Mr. Robbie Collins, Dean Watson, and other valuable members of the DISD business and administrative offices were also directly responsible for all administrative issues in organizing and delivering the program. Other DISD staff members, including the professional curriculum development division, were also very involved in working with CE staff to develop and produce all program materials.

Cooper Institute Staffing

As with the pilot program, Charles Sterling, executive director and CEO of the Cooper Institute, was ultimately responsible for all CI contractual involvement and reported all program information to Dr. Cooper. Tom was still administratively responsible for all CE involvement in the program and ultimately responsible for approving program administrative details. Steve Blair and his staff were still responsible for developing all research tools and instruments, monitoring these during the program delivery, collecting all statistical data, and writing, publishing, and presenting the scientific evidence of this program.

Roger was naturally assigned as program director. He reported directly to Tom at the CI and, in addition, coordinated all program activities with DISD Administrator Robbie Collins. In this manner of program coordination, Mr. Collins and Roger maintained a day-to-day interaction with each other while making sure that all program details and issues were being handled properly and reported accordingly. Both DISD and CI staff worked tirelessly side by side in the managing of all program scheduling, use of facilities, school and class timelines, equipment, class and book materials, gymnasium space, classroom space, CE staff break space, auditorium space, testing locations, etc. It was, in fact, a major coordination effort to provide the abovementioned actions in a successful manner.

Selection of the CE Professional Team to Deliver the Program

Because of the anticipated employee participation numbers, it was determined that a staff of twelve instructors was required to deliver the program. Potential candidates for these positions would only be those recommended by existing professional and executive staff of the Cooper Aerobics Center. It was believed that staff personal and professional experiences directly associated with the candidates would be a much better starting point than going with outside recommendations. In this manner, we were very fortunate to identify and hire the most highly qualified candidates from across the United States.

Candidates underwent an interview process that included a demonstration of their teaching skills by making a fifteen-minute presentation for evaluation. John's teaching expertise was critical in making the evaluations. Twelve individuals were selected as the "best of the best" instructors for our purpose. Those original twelve professionals nicknamed themselves the "Dirty Dozen" in respect to the enormous amount of work they would be asked to do. This nickname seemed to stick, as each of these twelve elite instructors underwent the most challenging and yet rewarding years of their professional careers. The DISD Dirty Dozen instructors were role models and without question were directly related to the enormous program success. These instructors were another example of Aerobic Center "missionaries." The following (both the original twelve and successive instructors) were the staff selected:

- Steve Farrell
- Marilu Meredith
- Mike Prentice
- Karyn Hughes
- Sara Van Amburgh
- Deb Strehle
- Lani Reed
- Charlotte Taylor
- Jill Upton
- Amy Schrickle
- Dr. Tom Wells
- Don Rainey

Additional staff were brought on board to replace and/or expand staff based on turnover and reassignment. They were:

- Mitch Bogdanffy
- Gary Knadler
- Rob Kahn
- Virginia Lamming
- Jean Storlie
- Julie White
- Dennis Flood
- Tom Siekman
- Nancy Anderson
- Barbara Gaydosh
- Tammy Sheperd

Professional Staff Training

A major theme of all CE programs was the importance of leadership. It was especially critical in enhancing exercise adherence. This was underscored by the staff training and development process for the selected instructors. A formal training program consisting of two weeks prepared these elite instructors for the task that awaited them. During the training, the skills detailed below were critical for each of the instructors to learn, practice, practice, and practice. Each instructor had to successfully accomplish the training tasks and responsibilities and demonstrate each required skill set, including the following:

- Presentation skills to successfully present an overview of the program to their assigned schools with the intended purpose of recruiting teachers to voluntarily participate.

- Skills associated with assessing and evaluating medical/health histories.

- Practical skills associated with conducting the fitness and medical assessments. Those required skills included assessing correct body weight, height, resting blood pressure, resting heart rate, body composition, flexibility, upper- and lower-body absolute strength, dynamic strength, and cardiovascular endurance. The two most complicated practical skills for each member to learn and successfully perform were the treadmill test (which included resting and exercise EKGs), and the art of drawing blood. Both of these skills challenged the instructors to the edge of frustration, patience, and high anxiety. However, after two weeks of training, these skills were finally and successfully mastered. It was noted, however, that almost every person on the Aerobics Center campus suddenly became victims (subjects) for these instructors who were looking for human subjects to serve as their "guinea pig".

- Interpretation skills of understanding each teacher's medical screening and fitness assessment scores were necessary to properly teach the group review session for participants in which they developed the teachers' individual "exercise and stress management" prescription.

- Skills of individual counseling techniques. During the initial stages of the program, the instructors met for thirty minutes with every teacher assigned to their schools to review their personal medical and fitness score and to set both short- and long-term goals for improvement and/or to maintain proper fitness levels.

- Behavior contracting motivational skills. As a scientifically proven motivational strategy, each instructor was taught how to explain, define, and assist each teacher on how to properly complete a "behavior contract," which would hold them accountable to their goals and program commitment. The contract would be signed by the teacher and instructor to ensure an agreed-upon commitment. This contract would then be reviewed with the teachers and instructor throughout the formal program to be assured that they were progressing correctly. It would include the teacher's personal goals, his or her selected accountability partner, and the specific responsibilities of the teacher and his or her chosen partner. Finally, the reward and contract timeline would be determined by the teacher.

- Teaching delivery skills. A very important part of each instructor's skill set was to learn the academic content he or she would be teaching. Eight education modules were defined based on the pilot program evaluation as the most valuable to be delivered in the weekly education/exercise sessions. The one-hour education modules consisted of the following:

  – Module #1: A Physical Program

- Module #2: The Concept of Wellness and Risk

- Module #3: Nutrition and Weight Control

- Module #4: Exercise—Aerobics

- Module #5: Exercise—Flexibility

- Module #6: Exercise—Strength

- Module #7: Stress Management and Relaxation

- Module #8: Fitness Maintenance

- Exercise leadership skills. The instructors were required to learn specific group exercise routines, including the proper biomechanics for the various exercises in a routine. All exercise routines were delivered to the teachers once a week immediately following the classroom educational module. In addition to the in-class exercise routines, the instructors were taught specific exercises to teach participating teachers that they could successfully do at home.

- Stress management techniques. Instructors learned guidelines on how to properly educate the teachers to successfully perform stress-management and relaxation strategies at home. The instructors were given skills and materials to help assist the teachers in identifying their personal stress sources, level of stress impact on their lives, and how to properly manage these stressors.

Each instructor was given a program workbook (manual) which would also be given to each teacher. This workbook would contain all information necessary to help the instructors understand and deliver all program information. It would serve not only as an important program manual to follow during the formal program, but also serve the teachers as an invaluable source of personal information and guide to a better life. Following these two weeks of intense training, the instructors were prepared and ready to deliver the program in 180 schools.

Question #4: How Did It Work?

Program briefings were provided at every DISD school site. In the first year, over 3,600 teachers signed up to participate (approximately one-third of all teachers). In addition, another 1,800 teachers/spouses registered for an evening program that included the same components that were included in the daytime teacher program. Both programs were delivered simultaneously.

The program was implemented in an identical fashion and sequence as the pilot program. Teachers underwent a twelve-week process consisting of the following elements at their respective schools:

- Pre-program assessment collection of personal health information on participants

- Pre-program health screening and fitness screening of each participant

- Individual fitness counseling

- Development of individual lifestyle exercise plans

- Twelve-week exercise and educational classes

- Post-program health and fitness assessment

- Final group discussion and feedback session with participants

Program Delivery

The instructional staff were organized into three teams of four instructors operating out of the various wellness centers at three schools: Hexter, De Goyler, and Nolan Estes Plaza. The wellness centers, in turn, served as the hub for the schools (with physical proximity) where the exercise and educational classes were delivered to the teachers. While the program delivery was identical for each center, each team developed its own strategies for delivering all the program components.

Participating teachers were assigned to one of three waves consisting of 1,500 teachers in each wave. Each instructor was assigned to manage and deliver the program to fifteen schools during the year. During the first wave of 1,500, teacher fitness assessments were administered from 8:00 a.m. to 5:00 p.m. daily in the assigned wellness center. The most difficult and time-consuming assessment was the cardiovascular endurance evaluation. This required approximately sixteen treadmill tests every day in each wellness center for a total of approximately forty-eight treadmill tests with ECG monitoring per day. This effort was unprecedented in the world of treadmill testing within a typical medical or corporate setting. Many people looking on from the outside could not believe that this would ever be possible, which is why the enormous success of the DISD employee fitness program became national news at the time.

Instructor Schedule

The work demands on the instructional staff were considerable. Morning activities revolved around conducting assessments and making specific school preparations. The afternoon tasks consisted of delivering the exercise and educational modules at those schools served by a given wellness center. To get a flavor for the work intensity, below is a typical daily schedule for an instructor:

4:00–4:30 a.m.	Rise and shine
5:30–6:00 a.m.	Arrive at wellness center—necessary if drawing blood was scheduled.

6:00 a.m.–2:00 p.m.   Tasks to be performed:
- Blood labs
- Cardiovascular endurance testing on treadmill
- All physical fitness assessments
- Follow-up for any teachers who missed an earlier appointment
- Confirm, adjust, or repair any equipment issues
- Assist any teacher with previous assessment concerns
- Work on assigned teacher personal program files
- Make necessary phone calls, etc. to assigned teachers
- Complete wellness center responsibilities for that day

12:00–1:00 p.m.   Lunch (time varied for each wellness center)
1:00–4:30 p.m.   Tasks to be performed (specific tasks varied for each wellness center):
- Prepare materials and equipment for afternoon classes
- Load needed equipment and take to assigned school
- Prepare the classroom for the education module
- Deliver the appropriate education module
- Deliver the appropriate group exercise class
- Collect any work previously assigned to teachers
- Confirm teachers' out-of-class exercise activity
- Confirm teachers' previous week aerobic point totals

           –   Ensure that classroom is cleared of all material
           –   Confirm teachers assigned to the program

5:00–6:00 p.m.   Depart assigned school at end of workday
           –   Instructors take all questionable ECGs to Cooper Clinic for medical review

The intensity of that schedule is presented to underscore the supreme effort and commitment of this staff and served as another example of the Aerobics Center "missionaries'" team effort and spirit.

Question #5: What Were the Results?

A full-scale evaluation was performed on the first-year iteration of the program; 3,846 teachers participated in the program, and pre- and post-program testing was performed on 2,632.

Physical Changes

Pre–post comparisons paralleled those found in the pilot program and showed significant changes in those teachers receiving the program. They made significant changes on a number of factors, including an 11 percent increase in daily physical activity, a 20 percent increase in abdominal strength, a 5 percent increase in upper-body strength, a 4 percent increase in leg strength, an 8 percent increase in flexibility, a 5 percent reduction in body fat, and a 17 percent increase in cardiovascular endurance.

Health Behaviors

Significant changes were also noted in several health behaviors. Eleven percent of those who smoked at the beginning of the program quit, while 26 percent of those initially sedentary teachers ended up following a vigorous exercise program. Most of the participants reported making dietary modifications that were reflected in an average waist girth reduction of a half inch following the program.

Psychosocial Changes

Pre- and post-program written surveys to assess a number of psycho-social factors also paralleled the results of the pilot program, showing that those participating in the program showed a significant increase in their general feeling of well-being, an increased job and overall life sat-isfaction, an increased sense of a positive self-concept, and an increase in energy level. In terms of handling stress, the participants reported a significant increase in being free from worry and feeling relaxed as opposed to being tense.

Implications for Workplace Absenteeism

A major finding was the relationship of participation to teacher absen-teeism. Cardiovascular fitness (as measured by treadmill time) was highly correlated with reduced absenteeism. Participants had 1.25 fewer ab-sent days than nonparticipants for the year, and the pre–post changes for participants were 1.47 fewer days from their base rate.

At that time, the cost for a substitute teacher in the DISD was $47 a day. Given the absenteeism rate for the 3,846 participants, the DISD saved $225,952 that year. If all teachers had participated (12,136) and had similar absenteeism statistics, an estimated $712,990 could have been saved per year.

These data convinced the DISD to partially underwrite the cost of the program in successive years to encourage more participation. The program continued for several additional years utilizing CI staff, after which a modification of the original program continued to be delivered by DISD staff with the CI advising.

Ultimate Implication

This program became one of the largest employee fitness programs of its kind in the United States and later proved to be the most suc-cessful by all measurable variables. It served as the Cooper Institute's watershed research application program as reported by CI scientists and provided a blueprint for similar programs across America. The

National School Boards Association recommended its further application in American schools.

The dedication of both the CI and DISD staff was responsible for these positive results. Teamwork and "going the extra mile" were the norm for all involved, and the DISD program served as the model and example of what can be achieved with "missionary" zeal and effort. During the initial stages of the program, there were many naysayers who voiced that implementing the program, let alone getting positive results, was an impossible task. More than any other Cooper Institute initiative, the DISD project provided the evidence that when a team of talented, selfless, and devoted professionals work together for a common goal, "the impossible becomes possible." We offer to each of the project staff the greatest appreciation and absolute respect for your professional excellence.

CREATION OF THE SPECIAL PROJECTS DIVISION AND FURTHER APPLICATIONS

Following the reported success of the DISD program, other school districts expressed interest. To meet that demand, a new division was created called Special Projects and was headed up by Mike Prentice, who had been one of the original Dirty Dozen. As a consequence, two local school districts contracted with the Cooper Institute to deliver the same program to their school districts. The Richardson Independent School District (RISD) and the Coppell Independent School District (CISD) subsequently were able to implement the program. In addition to these school programs, the New York City Schools also contracted with the Cooper Institute to consult with them on how they could deliver a modified version of this program to teachers within the New York City School System. Due to funding deficits at the time, an extensive evaluation was not able to be made on those iterations. However, subjective feedback indicated similar positive results along with both teacher and administrative written reports.

Roger's mother and brothers

Roger and wife Annette

Annette and Roger leading exercise class in Japan

Dr. Cooper with authors John, Roger and Tom

John and Roger teaching Law Enforcement Fitness Specialist
class at Ohio Peace Academy in London, Ohio

Flexibilit

by Dr. John R. Poteet, Ed.D., Ass
Continuing Education, Institute

Flexit
the le
stood a
troversi
ent of
ness. W
general
upon t
need f
of flexibility, some cont
concerning the best wa

John receiving outstanding achievement recognition
for flexibility instruction from Cooper Institute

John and wife Shirley

Roger teaching running drills to Air Force Fitness Instructors, Hill Air Force Base

Roger and James Patsellis teaching Command
Fitness Leader class for Navy in Guam

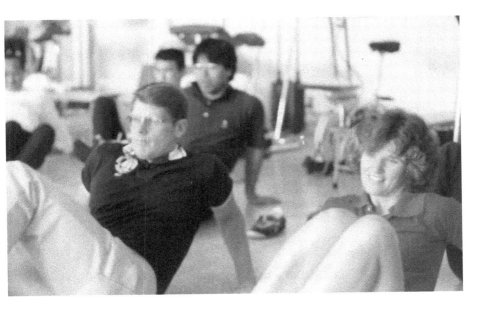

Tom and his wife Gretchen leading an exercise class

John and students at workshop graduation

Tom leading fun run in Japan

Tom testing police on the 1.5 mile run

Dr. Cooper, John, Roger, Tom and staff receiving the
Directors Honor award from the US Secret Service

Roger 80 and John 90 enjoying active retirement

A young Tom and John with Cooper Institute
professional education staff Nita and Susan

Tom teaching flexibility

Roger and children, Randy, Lisa, Shawn and Lance

CHAPTER 7

Consulting as an Outreach Service

As was mentioned in chapter 5, law enforcement and military requests for special consultative services from the Continuing Education Division expanded the scope of outreach services that the CE Division could provide. That effort resulted in the eventual emergence of a Program Services/Consultation Division to meet that need.

Question #1: What Need Was Met, and How Did That Need Become Apparent to Us?

Over time, many requests from a wide variety of government and non government organizations for consultative services were made. Based on the CE's experience of designing fitness programs for law enforcement agencies, initial requests from non-law enforcement organizations were for assistance in developing employee fitness and wellness programs. Later, as the "fitness industry boom" was growing, more organizations were looking for ways to provide a number of fitness/wellness services

Knowing of the success that the entire Cooper Aerobics Center (Clinic and Fitness Center) was having, requests were being made to aid in comprehensive program and facility design for medical clinics, hospitals, and fitness centers based on Dr. Cooper's model for the Cooper Clinic and Cooper Fitness Center.

Question #2: What Was the Aim?

The ultimate aim of institute services was to assist organizations to meet their goals in developing and implementing fitness/wellness services, be it for their employees, clients and patients, or health club members. It was also the goal to expand those efforts to enable the Cooper Institute to be a full-service organization that could help clients in a variety of ways by sharing the entire Cooper Aerobics Center expertise. Those services also enabled the institute to create additional revenue streams.

Question #3: What Did We Do?

Initial Services for Employee Fitness/Wellness Programs

At one level, the expansion of consultation outreach services was a continuation of the model applied to law enforcement and military clients. That same process was overlaid on civilian organizations with many of the identical elements tailored to their needs. The initial con-sultative services (especially for employee fitness/wellness programs) were delivered under the umbrella of the CE Division by Tom. Later, as part of the nursery concept, a separate consulting service under the total Cooper Aerobics Center was instituted, which, in turn, emerged into the Program Services Division within the institute to deliver those outreach services. All levels of consultant services involved a consultant team approach.

A systematic consultative process was defined that facilitated a given client through an exploration process, ultimately delineating a program that the organization could implement. There were eight basic phases to the process:

1. Initial planning

2. Definition of mission and goals for the program

3. Definition of program components

4. Definition of the resources necessary to deliver the defined programs

5. Definition of a budget

6. Definition of operational procedures and policies

7. Definition of a functional organizational structure

8. Definition of program evaluation process

The final step was the definition and delivery of a final report (sometimes called a concept paper) to a client documenting the entire process with specific recommendations for application and implementation of the program. Follow-up consultation aided in finalizing a client's plan, supporting their implementation, and troubleshooting. Our perspective was that a final report was not the end of the consultative process but the real beginning.

As part of the consultative process, the Personalized Aerobics Lifestyle System (PALS) was made available to clients. As mentioned in chapter 6 on the Aerobics Stress Management Program, a manual was developed for participants that covered a number of wellness areas such as exercise, nutrition, and stress management. That manual was reconfigured into a computerized version called the Personalized Aerobics Lifestyle System (PALS) that included a fitness assessment scoring card called FitCheck. The PALS system was implemented with many of the employee fitness programs that the institute consulted on.

Later Services

As the reputation of the Cooper Clinic and Cooper Fitness Center grew, requests started being made by medical clinics, hospitals, and health clubs seeking aid in "duplicating" the Cooper model. Hospitals, for example, were expanding into preventive medicine (wellness) services, developing in-house fitness facilities and rehabilitation centers. Tennis and racquetball centers were expanding into providing more total fitness and wellness services. In response to those requests, a consultative service under the total Cooper Aerobics Center was established.

Under the direction of Roger, a consulting team from the entire Cooper Aerobics Center was organized. It consisted of staff from the Cooper Fitness Center, including its director, Bill Grantham, and Cooper Clinic staff such as Gordon Henderson, nutritionist Jean Storlie, and physicians such as Dr. Larry Gibbons and Dr. Boyd Lyles. Roger would initiate client contacts and determine what their consultation needs were.

That process created a challenge that had to be met. Oftentimes, what a given client needed was a service that the existing team did not have the expertise to provide. The solution was to solicit and establish cooperative relationships with experts that could be part of the total consultant team. Relationships were established with Arthur Anderson accounting and several architects to provide additional expertise. This enabled the Cooper Aerobics Center consulting services to be individualized for each client.

Those consultation services were similar to the employee program consultation in that the overall process followed a structured sequence from initial planning to design and implementation. The biggest difference was that each client selected from a menu of twelve specific services based on their unique needs:

1. Facility design and development

2. Population density studies

3. Financial feasibility studies

4. Financial proformas

5. Marketing strategies

6. Design of service deliveries

7. Staffing

8. Staff training

9. Business operations

10. Marketing strategies

11. Budgeting strategies

12. Operational services

Question #4: How Did It Work?

There was no formal marketing of the consultative services. Primary contacts and potential leads for prospective clients were a direct result in most cases from Dr. Cooper's worldwide speaking engagements and major presentations at professional meetings. Additional potential clients made contact based on word of mouth, by having attended the Cooper Clinic, or having participated in a Continuing Education course at the Cooper Institute. An individual or organization would make contact with the consultant team, and the client was then followed up with to determine the necessary next step. There were two types of clients: specific service clients and retainer clients.

Specific Service Clients
These were clients who wanted a specific and typically one-time consultation, either for assistance in their employee fitness/wellness programs
or for those hospitals, health clubs, fitness centers, etc. to expand their
client wellness services. Once it was determined that the team could
assist a given client, a formal agreement (contract) was developed for
specific services, and the detailed consultation process was initiated.

Retainer Clients
These clients (primarily hospitals, clinics, or fitness centers) contracted
for a variety of services on an ongoing basis (one year at a time), with
minor exclusivity which provided them ongoing support and marketing
advantage. Because the "Cooper Aerobics Center" name would be affiliated with a potential client, each potential retainer client underwent
a detailed level of scrutiny to meet certain standards of service and
had to have a local Better Business Bureau favorable rating. As part of
the retainer service, a yearly review was conducted that afforded the
opportunity for follow-up, upgrades, troubleshooting, and revisions of
agreements if appropriate. The number of retainer clients was limited
to ten per calendar year. Utilizing this strategy allowed the consultant
team to quickly and efficiently manage these clients' various needs.

Question #5: What Were the Results and Implications?
Consultative services were provided to over fifty clients, including thirteen retainers, over the course of several years. Three of those retainer
clients were international, in Japan, Switzerland, and Italy. Those clients
receiving assistance with their employee fitness/wellness needs were
able to apply the recommended programs as fitness promotion strategies to improve the health and well-being of their employees. Other
organizations, including retainer clients, were able to utilize the consultative services to greatly expand and upgrade the wellness services
they could provide to their respective clients. While there is no way
of determining the ultimate number of employees, medical patients,

and fitness center members that benefited from our clients, it would definitely be in the thousands.

The later version of consulting services was highly profitable. As a consequence, it was eventually placed administratively under the Institute's Program Services Division, since the nonprofit institute needed additional revenue sources to support the research efforts. Regardless of the administrative placement, the consultation outreach served to further expand the impact of Dr. Cooper's model of preventive medicine, fitness, and total well-being.

CHAPTER 8

Youth Fitness Initiatives

The Cooper Institute made significant inroads in facilitating youth fitness over the years through two initiatives. The first was the FitnessGram computerized fitness assessment system, and the second was the First Choice exercise program for at-risk youth.

FITNESSGRAM

The importance of youth fitness had been recognized for years, ever since the original President's Council on Physical Fitness and Sports was established in the 1950s and '60s. Following the recommendations of that council, the American Alliance for Health, Physical Education, Recreation, and Dance (AAPHERD) for many years instituted a national fitness assessment program for school-aged youth that schools could apply to make use of. At about the time that the Cooper Institute was starting its outreach "missions" in the late 1970s and early 1980s, innovative computer-based learning systems were being developed, and it was recognized that there were significant implications for how to better assess students' physical fitness.

Question #1: What Need Was Met, and How Did That Need Become Apparent to Us?

The goal for the original fitness assessment programs in the schools was that they would provide the feedback necessary to encourage youth to increase their physical activity and consequent fitness. Surveys were indicating, however, that even though fitness assessments had been provided within schools, the fitness levels of youth were not improving but were, in fact, deteriorating. It became apparent that a new assessment approach was needed. In turn, the advent of computers offered an opportunity to upgrade and enhance the fitness assessment process.

Question #2: What Was the Aim?

The aim of FitnessGram was to develop the first computer-generated student fitness "report card." The intent was to provide teachers with a way to communicate the results of fitness assessments to students and parents. It needed to be a transportable program that could be applied within any school system by simply providing the software (computer discs) to a school. The ultimate goal was that the program would serve to enhance a school's physical education curriculum to increase youths' activity and fitness levels.

Question #3: What Did We Do?

The Cooper Institute had a model program to work from. Charles Sterling, before becoming the institute's executive director, had piloted the concept of a fitness report card while he was the physical education supervisor for a local school district. In turn, Marilu Meredith, also from the Cooper Institute, had worked with him in the past to develop the fitness report card. She was appointed the FitnessGram program director, and under her leadership, for several decades, the program grew to national and international prominence.

Initial Challenges

The major issue, at first, was to generate the funding for the project. Establishing partnerships for the development, promotion, and application of the program was the solution. Over the years, many private entities were beneficial in providing the needed support. First was the Campbell Soup Company, followed by the Prudential Insurance Company. Human Kinetics provided a publishing and distribution relationship that aided in national expansion. Dr. Greg Welk, as scientific director for FitnessGram, aided that effort. Cooperative relationships with the ACSM, AAPHERD, and President's Council on Physical Fitness and Sports also aided in eliciting school districts to utilize FitnessGram.

The next challenge involved all the planning aspects to determine the key components of what the project would entail. The initial planning involved discussions with Cooper Institute staff, and through the years, a scientific advisory group was established with representatives from professional groups such as the ACSM, AAHPERD, and the President's Council on Physical Fitness and Sports. Several key factors emerged from that group that were incorporated into the FitnessGram assessment system.

First was that the test battery should contain field tests that measure the health-related physical fitness areas that were defined through current research, such as Dr. Cooper's data, showing the necessity of fitness for overall health and well-being. Second was that the norms that were used should be revised from percentile measures to criterion measures. The previous AAHPERD assessment battery used percentile norms by age and gender so that a student was compared to his or her peer group along a continuum. It did not provide an index of what was considered healthy, just the concept that the higher the percentile, the better. Consequently, a determination was made that the scoring should be based on the minimal performance on a test that was necessary for health. That definition involved considerable research and discussion to define those levels. Third was to define associated curriculum guides for increasing fitness test performance. Fourth was the technical development of the computerized system and how it would work.

FitnessGram Test Items

The FitnessGram test battery has undergone revisions over the years to reflect ongoing research as to the major health-related areas and how best to measure them. The current battery measures the following areas with associated tests:

- Aerobic capacity: Three optional tests are used. Test times are converted to the VO2 max equivalency (mlO2/kg/min) that is used as the measure:

  - One-mile run

  - One-mile walk

  - The PACER test, which is a pace set to music that increases intensity over a twenty-meter shuttle run.

- Body composition: Two optional tests are used:

  - Skinfold measurement (percent fat)

  - Body mass index (ratio of height to weight)

- Muscular strength and endurance: Three separate tests are used:

  - Abdominal strength and endurance—curl-ups set to a specified pace

  - Trunk extensor strength—trunk lift in inches

  - Upper-body strength and endurance—push-ups or modified push-ups set to a specified pace

- Flexibility: two optional tests are used:

  - Back saver sit and reach in inches

  - Shoulder stretch—pass/fail

FitnessGram Performance Standards

As with the test battery, revisions have been made over the years. Currently, three standards are defined for each test. A Health Risk (HR) zone was set, indicating the level of fitness that places the student at a health risk, and a Needs Improvement (NI) score was also defined. A Healthy Fitness Zone (HFZ) performance standard was established that indicated the minimal fitness necessary for health. As was mentioned, each HFZ standard was based on what the Scientific Advisory Board established based on current research on fitness levels as indicators of health status.

Developing the FitnessGram Computerized Report Card System

Once the computer-based system was developed, the application of that system for schools was defined. After students were tested, an individual FitnessGram report card was generated for the student and parent. The card had activity tips and guidelines. The software allowed for a school to generate school-wide and district-wide summary reports. That data could be used to track trends and changes in students' fitness and examine associations between academic achievement, attendance, and fitness. In addition, communication between students' parents and teachers was enhanced. Finally, the FitnessGram data could be used to identify curriculum needs and areas for program funding.

Question #4: How Did It Work?

It was recognized from the beginning that for FitnessGram to be accepted, there would have to be many cooperative partnerships with schools to aid in promoting and applying the program.

Implementing FitnessGram

In the beginning, a pilot program was instituted with the Tulsa, Oklahoma school district, and the program methods were refined from that experience. Over the years, many manuals of instruction were produced to enable schools and physical education teachers to do the fitness testing and use the computerized recording process.

For schools applying the program, the process was not labor intensive. Once a school agreed to implement the program, the software was provided, and the self-instructional materials/manuals allowed for easy installation. Participating schools and districts were to forward data back to the CI, and while that was not always consistent, much data over the years has been incorporated into a growing database for analyzing FitnessGram results and effects over time.

Expanded Programming

Over the years, many enhancements were made to the basic assessment program in recognition of the ultimate goal of increasing physical activity among students. Teachers were encouraged to use test performance to recognize improvement as a motivation tool. Examples were the "FitnessGram Honor," "Get Fit," and "Fit for Life" awards. In cooperation with AAPHERD, a fitness recognition system titled "You Stay Active" was developed along with activity and curriculum ideas for schools.

The link between fitness assessment and physical activity led to the development of a similar computerized report card called ActivityGram. A Previous Day Physical Activity Recall form was used to monitor mode, frequency, and intensity of activity. A simplified version titled Youth Activity Profile (YAP) was also developed. Most recently, FitnessGram teamed up with the NFL Play 60 program to help promote youth daily physical activity to combat obesity. In turn, FitnessGram collaborates with the Play 60 longitudinal study to assess the long-term effectiveness of those initiatives to increase youth physical activity and fitness.

The Cooper Institute has also recently partnered with the greater Dallas area United Way to support and recognize schools in fighting the childhood obesity epidemic and creating healthy school environments. Besides the fitness assessment program, a variety of educational resources are being provided Dallas-area schools.

FitnessGram also expanded internationally with the development of the Cooper International Youth Fitness Test that was piloted in China. In addition, a cooperative agreement was established with the Hungarian School Sport Federation to create a national fitness test.

Question #5: What Were the Results and Implications?

While an accurate estimate of the number of schools that have participated is not available, every school district in some states such as California, Texas, Florida, Delaware, and many more were required to administer FitnessGram. Thousands of teachers have used and millions of students have received FitnessGram assessments (some years have reported ten million students a year) over the last thirty-five years. Various school districts have reported improved academic achievement and attendance associated with improved fitness levels. The NFL Play 60 longitudinal study noted that youth participating in that program had improved aerobic capacity and body mass indices when compared to youth in schools not participating in the program.

The FitnessGram program has received many national recognition awards, and Charles Sterling, the program's founder, received the President's Council on Physical Fitness and Sports Presidential Lifetime Achievement Award in recognition for his innovative efforts to support youth fitness.

The ultimate goal of school-based fitness programs is to improve the physical activity and fitness levels of students, and a key component of such a total fitness program is the fitness assessment. To achieve improved activity and fitness, one needs to first know current fitness status (know where one is) before setting improvement goals (where one needs to be). Likewise, a post-program assessment provides the feedback as to reaching or not reaching the fitness goals. While the exercise programs, teacher leadership, and reinforcement systems are all important elements of a fitness program, FitnessGram has demonstrated that it has and continues to meet the need for the valid assessment element.

FIRST CHOICE FITNESS PROGRAM FOR AT-RISK YOUTH

The 1980s saw an increased concern about how to counter substance abuse by youth. The "war on drugs" was initiated at many levels, and the Cooper Institute enlisted in that war.

Question #1: What Need Was Met, and How Did That Need Become Apparent to Us?

The term "at-risk youth" has normally been applied to disadvantaged youth in inner cities and poverty areas. At a general level, it referred to being at risk of dropping out of school, criminal activity, substance abuse, and lack of economic opportunity. The data on substance abuse in the 1980s, however, led many to believe that all youth were to be considered to be at risk. As a consequence, a variety of programs were initiated in and out of the school environment; however, trends were indicating little success. Data indicated that the use of "gateway drugs" (alcohol, cigarettes, and marijuana) set the stage for the more serious use of drugs such as heroin, cocaine, etc., and that became the major focus of prevention efforts.

Prior to coming to the Cooper Institute, Tom had delivered several fitness programs aimed at at-risk youth with substance abuse, delinquency, and mental health problems. The results of those programs documented that exercise can positively affect many risk factors for those conditions and reduce substance abuse and delinquent behavior. Knowing of his experience, the Allstate Foundation approached Tom to develop a pilot fitness program for at-risk youth specially aimed at preventing and reducing substance abuse. That program served as the Continuing Education's initial efforts to address this problem that led to many later program installations.

Question #2: What Was the Aim?

The fitness program titled 1st Choice was first and foremost a physical fitness and exercise intervention. The program was based on the assumption that at any point in time, a youth can be viewed as developing either a health-compromising or health-enhancing lifestyle. Likewise, youth behavioral problems can be viewed as but symptoms of an unhealthy lifestyle. The development of a more active and fit lifestyle was seen as a basic step to aid development and to offset health-compromising behaviors such as substance abuse.

The goals of the program were sequentially ordered to first increase physical activity and consequently fitness. Second was to structure the exercise process to teach participating youth the values of respect, responsibility, and self-discipline and to teach assessment, goal setting, and planning life skills. Third was to positively affect substance abuse risk factors such as self-concept and well-being. By focusing on these basic elements in the physical domain, program participants would make positive gains in physical fitness and activity that would generalize to other behaviors and specific problem areas (such as substance abuse).

In terms of program application, the ultimate aim was to install 1st Choice in a wide variety of settings serving at-risk youth. Prevention locations included YMCAs, Boys and Girls Clubs, recreation centers, and school sites such as alternative and after-school programs established to serve at-risk youth. Other community sites included public health agencies and National Guard Drug Demand Reduction programs implemented through their armories. More focused treatment locations included residential and community drug abuse sites, mental health sites, and juvenile justice settings, including correctional institutions, law enforcement diversion, and probation sites.

An interesting sidelight occurred in some of the school settings. Physical education (PE) programs within many school settings were not always getting fiscal and administrative support for their curriculum and activities. In too many schools, PE was considered a lower priority. However, when some of the schools we approached to consider 1st Choice as a PE program to prevent drug abuse, they enthusiastically agreed to apply it. It would appear that if a physical fitness program is crafted and promoted to meet what a client sees as an important need, then it is more likely to be accepted.

Question #3: What Did We Do?

<u>Program Design</u>
Using the past programs developed by Tom as a model, the 1st Choice program curriculum was defined that contained the following components:

- Group exercise classes

- Twenty-four educational modules to teach participants "life skills," including assessing one's personal fitness level, goal setting, individual exercise planning, self-monitoring, nutrition, stress management, substance abuse, and violence prevention. A "Taking Charge" workbook was designed for participants to utilize in applying the module content.

- A behavior-contracting module where youth would agree to follow and sign a "Code of Conduct" to practice the values of respect, responsibility, and self-discipline.

Because the program was arranged on a modular basis, it could be applied by a given site in a variety of ways in terms of days per week, duration of each session, and number of weeks. Most sites delivered the program three days a week, one hour per session for twelve weeks.

Additional support components were defined that were not applied in all settings but were available to participating sites to utilize if warranted:

- A peer leader program teaching selected youth to assume program responsibilities such as being a group exercise leader. This was used as a major motivational strategy for participants.

- A parent education program providing three modules: 1) behavior contracting with your child to gain control, 2) family fitness activities, and 3) how to follow a personal walking exercise program to serve as a role model for your child.

Program evaluation was a necessity to document the effects so that funding could be solicited and sustained. This was a major "selling point" for 1st Choice. There were many drug abuse prevention programs operating at the time, but most had no evaluation and consequent justification for their continuation. Incorporating evaluation into 1st Choice separated it from other programs. An assessment and evaluation system was created to allow for pre–post comparisons, including fitness and activity assessment, self-report substance abuse risk factors assessment (self-concept and well-being), self-report substance use, and parent and/or school assessment of attendance and grades.

Pilot Programs

A pilot program was initiated with the original Allstate Foundation grant at three representative sites in the Dallas area: an alternative school for at-risk youth, a community drug abuse counseling agency, and an in-residence substance abuse treatment facility. Both Tom and Roger delivered the pilot program components over a twelve-week period. The lessons learned from the pilot were incorporated into revisions of the curriculum that would eventually be applied in future installations nationwide. In addition, Roger delivered the program to students assigned to the Richardson ISD alternative school and the W.T. White High School in the DISD for one semester.

Results from those pilot programs showed that increasing fitness was the key factor for a variety of positive changes in substance abuse risk factors and use patterns. Those youth who improved their fitness, when compared to those who didn't, demonstrated a significant increase in self-esteem and well-being; had significantly less drug, alcohol, and cigarette usage per week; and had significantly more total abstainers from using any of the gateway drugs.

Expanded Programs

Following the pilot programs' documented success, additional grants were obtained, and installations were made in numerous sites in several states and cities (Chicago, Illinois; Washington, DC; Roanoke, Virginia; Buffalo, New York; and Pittsburgh, Pennsylvania). The largest number of installations were made in the state of Illinois. The executive director of the Illinois Governor's Council on Physical Fitness, Jeff Sunderlin, was able to mobilize and solicit funding for many entities to implement 1st Choice. The largest-scale application was through the Illinois National Guard (NG) Drug Demand Reduction mission (at the time a major NG mission in each state), which delivered the program as an after-school program through its armories.

Major John Boatman and Colonel Chris Lawson were instrumental in expanding the program to be an outreach of the NG to equip community agencies to also deliver 1st Choice. A forty-hour master trainer course and curriculum to train selected National Guardsmen to, in turn, train others in their communities were designed. Unfortunately, 9/11 intervened, and all state NGs no longer provided drug demand reduction programming but were called up for active duty in the Middle East.

Question #4: How Did It Work?

Organizations wanting to implement the 1st Choice program would contact the Cooper Institute's Continuing Education Division. The first thing that had to be determined was the funding mechanism for the program. At all implementation sites, the program, once installed, was to become a part of their existing services. There were two major funding areas to address. The first was program staffing. The model for implementation at almost all sites was that existing staff would deliver the program, and the organization was able to absorb staffing costs as part of their services. The other costs were for the institute's services to install, monitor and support the program.

Leadership was viewed as the key to successful program installation with a focus on preparing and supporting an organization's staff to deliver the program. Cooper Institute services consisted of 1) provision of a forty-hour training course for staff that was similar to the Continuing Education Fitness Specialist course with additional content specific to 1st Choice; 2) provision of lesson plan curriculum and manuals; 3) data collection and program evaluation; and 4) ongoing support with follow-up training. Most of the organizations served either had already obtained funding or had to solicit grants and donations to obtain the needed finances. In some cases, the CI assisted in that effort. Over the years the CI was able obtain grants from numerous sources such as the Nancy Reagan Foundation, Illinois Department of Substance Abuse, National YMCA, and National Guard Bureau.

Following the training of an organization's staff, the CI would troubleshoot any implementation issues and usually have a one-day upgrade/discussion meeting with staff every six months. Sites would duplicate necessary forms, etc. and forward pre–post data to the CI for analysis. A one-year evaluation report would then be generated with recommendations for further application.

1st Choice Challenges

Since 1st Choice was leader driven, the problem of staff turnover was of major concern. As an organization lost trained staff, the problem of continually training new staff was an issue. The solution was to apply the master trainer concept previously mentioned regarding the NG program. That issue was compounded by the fact that applications of 1st Choice were very dependent on grant funding to participating organizations. Over time, the priority and funding for substance abuse programs declined, and it became increasingly difficult to secure the backing to continue spreading and expanding the program.

Sometimes you never know what could be a glitch in implementing a program, especially when the glitch was about different interpretations of words. Tom was scheduled to train some schoolteachers to apply the 1st Choice youth fitness program for a junior high school in Illinois. He was making a presentation to the superintendent of schools and discussed how the 1st Choice program used exercise to teach values and how the kids in the program were confronted to make an "admit and commit" statement if they didn't live up to the values. The superintendent stated that his school could not do the program because he didn't want the school to be teaching values, and kids should never be made to feel "guilty." Tom had to explain that the values were respect, responsibility, and self-discipline and that the kids signed a behavior contract to commit to practicing those values. The superintendent then agreed that was acceptable as long as the values were presented as "generic" and not religious.

Although in a different context from the youth fitness program, the problem of translation and interpretation of words once had had a very comical twist. Tom was at a hotel in Italy discussing with the manager if it was possible to conduct a seminar at his hotel. They were going over many potential details, and Tom often referred to the need for a setting for joggers to run and to provide the 1.5-mile run. As he kept using the word "jogger," he could tell the hotel manager appeared confused. Finally, the manager said he didn't understand what having a place for "jokers" was about. He asked if we were going to bring in some clowns or comedians for the program. While that misinterpretation was resolved, it became clear that the hotel would not be a good seminar site.

Question #5: What Were the Results and Implications?

Programs were installed in eighty-nine sites in seven states serving approximately ten thousand youth. The collective results of the evaluations (some published in peer reviewed journals) demonstrated a "chain of effect." Increased activity and fitness levels had a positive impact on substance abuse risk factors such as increased self-concept, well-being, school attendance, and grades. In turn, there were lowered substance abuse use patterns for alcohol, cigarettes, marijuana, smokeless tobacco, and multiple drug use. Finally, total abstinence was significantly increased.

The 1st Choice program received considerable recognition over the years for its effects. It was cited as one of the twenty exemplary youth fitness programs at the National Youth Fitness Summit and was selected for the National Registry of Effective Prevention Programs by the Center for Substance Abuse Prevention. The 1st Choice program delivered by the Illinois National Guard was cited as the model NG program for demonstrating the positive effects of the military's mission of drug demand reduction, and an iteration at an alternative school was recognized as the best physical education program for at-risk youth in the state of Texas.

The American College of Sports Medicine cited the program for further application nationwide to meet the Public Health Service Healthy People goals, which highlights the ultimate implication for what was learned and its value. Physical activity programs can be structured to meet many other health goals than just physical fitness. It reinforces Dr. Cooper's original belief and thesis that "exercise is medicine." At-risk youth, unfortunately, are underserved in meeting many of their needs, of which substance abuse is one of the most devastating. By focusing on the exercise dimension, untold benefits in other areas are not only possible but, based on the research, also probable.

CHAPTER 9
The Faith Connection

Dr. Cooper has a deep sense of faith. He was active in the Baptist Church and often spoke at church events, including in Billy Graham's international crusades. His faith permeated the entire Cooper Aerobics Center operation in many ways. He always set the tone for Cooper Aerobics Center staff meetings by offering a prayer before each meeting. The prayer's focus was on giving thanks for all the blessings given to staff efforts and petitions to apply for wisdom and energy to do our work. When there were occasions for staff meals together, he would ask Dr. Dick Bohannan to say grace. Dr. Bo (as the staff called him) would always make a request for nourishment of our bodies, our minds, and our spirits to meet our obligations to our "mission" and to God. The tone of these faith-based expressions was not an attempt to evangelize or force staff into a religious posture but was a humble acknowledgment that God played a role in our efforts.

Following the release of Dr. Cooper's bestselling book *Faith-Based Fitness*, there was a significant increase in awareness of physical fitness as it related to one's faith. Dr. Cooper always maintained that his career was truly blessed with "divine intervention," which without a doubt had a direct impact on his successful career. His book provided many reasons for and studies and scientific evidence of how faith and fitness were so similar. To quote a phrase from the cover of his book, "*Faith-Based Fitness* is a medical program that uses spiritual motivation to achieve maximum health and add years to your life." His bottom-line message regarding the faith connection was the importance of maintaining a balance of mind, spirit, and body, which requires an action-oriented lifestyle.

That faith connection was translated into missionary outreach efforts in which two of the CI staff (Roger and Tom) provided educational programs focusing on health and fitness from a faith perspective. While the participants of these programs were from two different church affiliations (Baptist and Catholic), the programs reflected their common Christian beliefs and tradition. Each outreach will be treated separately.

"JUST AS I AM": FITNESS AND WELLNESS PROGRAM FOR MINISTERS

As was mentioned, Dr. Cooper was very much involved with the Baptist Church in Dallas. He was very good friends with Dr. Jack Graham, pastor of Prestonwood Baptist Church, and Gene Greer, an official with the Southern Baptist Convention. They shared many civic and social moments together discussing the common elements of the physical and mental demands of leadership within their respective professions and the implications for following the Christian lifestyle. They approached Dr. Cooper with a health concern regarding Baptist ministers that eventually led to an outreach program for Baptist ministers that would be delivered by Roger.

Question #1: What Need Was Met, and How Did That Need Become Apparent to Us?

Their meeting was established to discuss the concern that both of them had expressed about the health and fitness conditions of the Southern Baptist Convention ministers. There were many examples presented of how the lack of fitness and exercise by pastors affected their overall well-being and the consequent impact on their ministerial duties. It was decided that a fitness/wellness program would be a positive attempt to address these concerns. Dr. Cooper recommended that Roger meet with Gene to discuss strategies for implementing such a program. Roger had, for several years prior to coming to the Cooper Aerobics Center, worked with Christian-related fitness programs in Indiana, Michigan, Illinois, and Ohio. Likewise, his experience directing the Fitness and Stress Management Program for teachers provided a direction for the needed program.

Question #2: What Was the Aim?

The program, to be titled "Just as I Am" Fitness and Wellness Program for Ministers, was to be provided to pastors and their spouses. In many respects, the aim of the program resembled the model of the DISD teacher program. The goal was to educate participants about the need for exercise and fitness and provide them with the proper guidelines for developing and maintaining a fit, healthy, and active lifestyle.

Question #3: What Did We Do?

Since the basic process for the program was the DISD program model, little design planning was required. Once all the arrangements were made for applying that model at the Cooper Clinic and Cooper Institute, the program was presented to prospective participants. Ministers, associate ministers, and spouses within the Southern Baptist Convention were invited to the Cooper Institute to hear a presentation on the details of the proposed program, after which they would volunteer to participate.

Core Program

Participants underwent a six-step process over a seven-day period consisting of the following elements:

- Medical screening: Each participant received a medical screening at the Cooper Clinic consisting of a maximal treadmill test, blood work, body composition, resting blood pressure, and resting heart rate vitals.

- Fitness assessments: Following the screening they received fitness assessments including flexibility, absolute muscular strength, dynamic muscular strength, step test endurance, and the one-mile walk test.

- Goal setting: Each participant received a thirty-minute individual counseling session reviewing all medical and fitness assessments and establishing goals for each category of health and fitness.

- Exercise and nutrition prescription: Each participant was given a workbook that included all program information, worksheets, exercise and nutrition logs, aerobic point charts, forms, general information, and Cooper Institute data to use as reference and comparison for their personal scores. During this session, personal exercise and nutritional recommendations and goals were discussed and decided upon by instructors and participants working together.

- Education modules: Following the recording of all program data into the participant's personal workbook, a series of nine education modules were delivered over the next several days. These educational lectures included the following: Medical Screening, Coronary Risk, Stress and Relaxation, Anatomy, Cardiovascular Training, Resistive Training, Flexibility Training, Exercise and Safety, and Nutrition.

- Motivation and behavior contracting planning: The final educational module included the application of a behavior contract and the identification of the stages of behavior change that they should expect.

Those elements were delivered over a seven-day period of one- to two-hour sessions at the Cooper Clinic and Cooper Institute. In the opening session, Dr. Cooper gave a very motivational and educational presentation, which set a very positive and Christian tone to the class. Participants left the formal program with a fitness and wellness plan to follow and then came back after six weeks for a refresher and review session.

Six-Week Follow-Up Session
All participants returned in six weeks for a review and discussion of their assigned work. They were also given a new fitness assessment, established new goals, and renewed and signed their behavior contract. At this progress session, Roger taught a lesson on identifying primary triggers participants were experiencing that could lead to drop out. Therefore, a considerable amount of time was spent in reviewing the "stages of change" from the earlier behavior modification/motivation class. The session ended with a group hug and the participants agreeing that they would "stay the course and keep the faith."

Program Continuation
A planning process was initiated to provide further assistance. It was agreed that a person within each church would be assigned to help continue providing assistance for all program participants. Roger would maintain contact with this assigned staff member to help when necessary. In addition, many of the churches agreed to subcontract with Cooper Certified Exercise Leaders to lead their group exercise classes. Ongoing contact encouraged each church to provide regular programs of activities—including joining local fun runs, in-house exercise classes,

sports leagues, health fairs, etc.—to keep the interest up, especially to support the notion of having fun while staying active.

A wellness committee was established within each church. Members became responsible for promoting the program throughout the church and keeping everything organized. The church wellness committee would report to the ministers or selected delegates to discuss all program components as things went forward. To assist their efforts, Roger was available to provide consultation and programming ideas. One example that was a key aid was the national calendar published every year, which provided a theme of health, fitness, and wellness every month with suggested activities and events that could be promoted.

National Southern Baptist Convention Annual Meeting

Dr. Cooper highlighted the original "Just as I Am" Fitness and Wellness Program during his keynote speech at the Southern Baptist Convention annual meeting. He explained the details and applications of the program and results achieved. He again reminded the audience of the statistical evidence and importance of maintaining proper fitness and wellness habits for all ministers and associate ministers. The attendees were overwhelmingly receptive to his remarks, which led to numerous ministers expressing a serious interest in providing this program at their church. Cooper Institute staff had a booth set up for attendees to come by and visit, receive printed material about the program, ask questions, and seek information for following up with them. Several churches requested follow-ups.

Question #4: How Did It Work?

The program was a coordinated effort between the Southern Baptist Convention (SBC) staff and the Cooper Aerobics Center staff. The SBC functions as a service agency to support Baptist ministers in a variety of ways, with pastor development a key area. SBC staff promoted the program by communicating directly to ministers to elicit participation and to provide ongoing communication to support the program.

Cooper Clinic and Cooper Institute staff provided the direct programming. The class sessions and follow-up contacts were provided predominately by Roger, and his leadership was instrumental in implementing all phases of the program.

The program was funded through the support of Gene Greer, and many of the services were provided on a gratis basis.

Question #5: What Were the Results and Implications?

The program was provided to three groups of ministers serving approximately ninety pastors and associate pastors. While a formal program evaluation was not undertaken, participant feedback indicated that 38 percent lost weight, 46 percent lost body fat, over 30 percent improved dynamic and absolute strength, and 36 percent improved cardiovascular endurance. Participants also submitted numerous positive comments. Most comments primarily focused on how the program had opened their eyes to the importance of achieving and maintaining a successful health, wellness, and active lifestyle. They also highlighted how the educational modules helped them to reach their personal goals.

Since the initial "Just as I Am" Fitness and Wellness Program was delivered to the Southern Baptist Convention Ministers, various types of similar programs emerged. An example was the "Wellness Day" initially provided and underwritten by the First United Methodist Church of Richardson, Texas. This one-day program included the following components: resting blood pressure and resting heart rate assessment, classroom lectures based on specific requested fitness topics, serving of a healthy lunch, social time, exercise classes based again on what types of classes were requested, question-and-answer time for open discussion, and, finally, a presentation by Dr. Cooper. Dr. Clayton Oliphint and his staff were very supportive of the Wellness Day event, and Roger was able to follow up by providing an in-house exercise instruction session for all participants.

Faith Implications

In the experience of providing the "Just as I Am" Fitness and Wellness Program for Baptist ministers, the scriptural basis for being fit and active was often highlighted. The Baptist faith relies heavily on looking at scriptural direction for one's efforts. Below are several of the biblical versus discussed in the program:

2 Timothy 4:7–8	For I have fought the good fight, I have finished the race, I have kept the faith.
Proverbs 4:23	Above all else guard your heart for it is the wellspring of life.
Ecclesiastes 9:11	The race is not to the swift or the battle to the strong, nor does food come to the wise or wealth to the brilliant or favor to the learned, but time and chance happens to them all.
1 Corinthians 6:19–20	Do you not know that your body is a temple of the holy spirit who is in you, whom you have received from God? Therefore, honor God with your body.
1 Timothy 4–8	Physical training is of some value but godliness has value for all days.
James 2:14	What good is it my brothers if a man claims to have faith but no deeds?
James 2:17	In the same way, faith by itself if it is not accompanied by action it is dead!

The Christian faith demands action (or effort) to continually practice the Christian life. Two words express that commitment to action: walk and faith. Being part of the body of Christ means submitting to be a willing and healthy vessel that God can work through to reach others who are in need. Faith minsters have the added obligation to fulfill their missionary vocation. The "Just as I Am" Fitness and Wellness Program served as a valuable step toward that goal.

SPIRIT, MIND, AND BODY AS A FOUNDATION FOR FITNESS: STEWARDSHIP OF NATURE AND THE BODY

This outreach, delivered by Tom, had a slightly different perspective and was aimed at three groups of Catholics: clergy, seminarians, and laity.

Question #1: What Need Was Met, and How Did That Need Become Apparent to Us?

During his pontificate, Pope St. John Paul II had a profound impact in many areas, but two that he spoke much about were caring for creation and caring for the body. He had a long history of being an outdoorsman and engaging in vigorous physical activity. In addition, he made several addresses to various sports groups on the value of exercise from a spiritual perspective. While John Paul II served as a great role model for a faith-based lifestyle, his teachings did not filter down to many Catholics, especially the clergy (priests, deacons, bishops, and religious orders).

A Faith-Based Need

Surveys had shown that that many Catholic clergy and seminarians were overweight, sedentary, and heavy smokers. Those same data indicated that the 24-7 nature of a parish priest's obligations provided much stress with little time to be concerned with one's personal health. Tom mentioned those surveys to a priest friend and shared that he always felt a deep sense of gratitude for the selflessness of priests. Many have a sense that their personal needs take second place to helping the "flock," and he remarked that a program to teach priests that to better serve parishioners, they need energy and should follow a personal fitness program would enable them to be of better service.

That priest (Father Bill) in turn challenged him to provide a day-long retreat on physical fitness for his diocesan parish priests and their seminarians. That started his involvement in providing fitness seminars and retreats for clergy as, in his words, "a way of offering a payback and thanks to the many priests who have served him."

Likewise, Pope St. John Paul II has been called the first "environmental pope" because of his advocacy of stewardship of nature. He made several addresses on that topic and made it the theme for one of his yearly World Day of Peace messages. At about the same time, Tom was volunteering as a master naturalist and Park Service ranger conducting nature projects. He became associated with an order of Catholic lay brothers from Peru who were part of the Christian Life Movement. One of their major apostolates (missions) was called CREATIO and had a focus on environmental stewardship to protect God's creation. As part of St. John Paul II's "New Evangelization," they recognized the need to provide outreach seminars and retreats for Catholic laypersons and clergy to engage in a nature stewardship lifestyle. Tom was recruited to get involved in that effort.

Question #2: What Was the Aim?

The focal point of the physical fitness dimension is energy. From a faith perspective, clergy and the lay faithful need that energy to fulfill Jesus Christ's simple commandment found in the Gospel of Mark (12:29–31): "love God and love your neighbor." The caring for and stewardship of our bodies and of the environment around us are necessary elements of that Christian obligation.

Two programs were developed. The first, titled "Spirit, Mind, and Body: A Faith Foundation for Fitness," had as its aim to increase the awareness of the need for exercise and fitness from a faith perspective and to provide guidelines for implementing a personal fitness and activity program. In the case of clergy and seminarians, the focus was on having the energy to fulfill their vocation to serve God and their parishioners. As an offshoot of this program, an additional group, the Knights of Columbus (a lay service order of the Church) received the program with the theme of having the energy to provide the order's many charitable services.

The second program, "Stewardship of Nature and the Body," had as its aim to assist primarily the laity to develop a nature stewardship lifestyle. As it was being developed, it was soon realized that to be a nature steward required energy and consequent physical fitness and that being active and fit is identical to being a steward of your own body. The stewardship processes for nature and the body have many parallels, and the two themes were linked together in that program. The aim of the program was similar to the first program regarding fitness, with an additional aim of providing a background on the needs of nature, environmental stewardship principles, and activities. While the original aim was at lay adults who would serve as "parish stewards" to apply what was learned to doing parish stewardship projects, it soon got expanded to be incorporated into Catholic school-based student outdoor education curriculums.

Question #3: What Did We Do?

While the two programs shared common elements in regard to fitness and exercise, the presentation of material and seminar/retreat activities were different for each.

Spirit, Mind, and Body: A Faith Foundation for Fitness

The seminar focus was on developing a fitness lifestyle and was presented within the framework of it being a necessity for having the energy to fulfill the obligations of priestly or charity vocations. The faith-based theme presented was taken from the Apostle Paul's first letter to the Corinthians (3:16)—"Do you not know that your body is the temple of the Holy Spirit within you?"—to illustrate a faith connection to the concept of physical fitness. Additional scriptural references were provided to illustrate that God intends for us to be active and to have a unity of body and soul, and with that comes a responsibility to care for our bodies.

The program was designed as a one-day seminar, and as the content was being organized, it got expanded into a book titled *Spirit, Mind, and Body: A Christian Foundation for Fitness*, which contained the material from the seminar lectures and practical exercises. The seminar and book content consisted of the following topics:

- The nature of wellness and fitness

- Overcoming exercise deficit disorder through stewardship of the body

- Self-assessment with a health risk appraisal

- The physical rationale for fitness and exercise

- The mental rationale for fitness and exercise

- The spiritual and faith-based rationale for fitness and exercise

- Health screening

- Fitness assessment and goal setting

- Designing an exercise plan

- Designing a motivational plan

Participants got a copy of the book, and during the course of the day, they worked through the exercises in the book, which involved a fitness assessment, setting fitness goals, and designing an exercise plan to follow. In some cases, it was arranged for the participating priests to have a six-month free membership at the local YMCA as an added incentive to "get moving."

Stewardship of Nature and the Body

The primary focus of this program was on the concept of stewardship. The faith-based theme presented was taken from the first two chapters of Genesis, where it is revealed that it is through following the human stewardship obligation that God's creation (nature) will be preserved. In Genesis 1:28, the notion of "subduing the earth" is linked to fruitfulness, and in Genesis 1:22–24, that fruitfulness is extended to other living creatures. In other words, subduing the earth implies a responsibility for the continuation, care, and well-being of all life. That is the Christian concept of environmental stewardship. It is not a call to leave the natural world alone. It is a call to care for it, as denoted in Genesis 2:15: "The Lord God then took the man and settled in the Garden of Eden, to cultivate and care for it."

A two- to three-day retreat was designed. As with the previous seminar, the material was encompassed into a book titled *Becoming a Creation Steward: A Catholic Ethic for the Environment*. While elements of the previous program were incorporated into this program, there was a different framework for presenting the material. The retreat process followed two separate tracks. The first focused on overcoming nature deficit disorder to be a steward of the environment and the second on overcoming exercise deficit disorder to be the steward of one's body. For each track a three-step process was presented that provided the framework for developing a stewardship lifestyle: encountering, exploring, and engaging.

The Three Steps for Developing a Faith-Based Stewardship Ethic

The program activities for the three steps in developing stewardship of the body were as follows:

- Encountering the body. This was encouraged by experiencing and observing the body's reactions to strenuous physical activity. Participants underwent physical exercise and monitored heart rate, muscle movements, fatigue, etc., then received information on how the body responds to movement. This was accomplished by participants reflecting on the body's response to being stressed through exercise.

- Exploring health/fitness issues and ethics. This involved increasing the awareness of one's level of physical activity and fitness and a faith-based physical, mental, and spiritual base for being fit. Participants underwent fitness assessments and goal-setting activities in this step.

- Engaging the body. This was the action element where concern motivated practicing a lifestyle of exercise and nutrition to develop energy and dynamic health. Participants designed programs that included fitness training regimens and tips for incorporating physical activity into daily life.

The program activities for the three steps in developing stewardship of nature were as follows:

- Encountering God's creation and nature. The process of encountering was to awaken enthusiasm for nature and to have a familiarity with and appreciation of creation. This was accomplished through participants taking focused nature hikes.

- Exploring environmental issues and ethics. This involved increasing the awareness of major environmental issues, the human role in them, and a faith-based ethic for addressing them. This was achieved by participants evaluating their personal lifestyle and community needs.

- Engaging creation. This was the action element where concern motivates stewardship actions individually and collectively to look at what can be done by asking a series of questions: What can we reduce? What can we reuse? What can we eliminate or substitute? What can we create or initiate? This was realized by participants developing stewardship plans around these questions.

A model was provided that showed conceptually how stewardship of the environment and the body are viewed as parallel endeavors. One is aimed toward ensuring a "fit" environment or creation and the other ensures a fit body. The following table was provided for discussion to illustrate that commonality:

PARALLEL CONCEPTS BETWEEN PERSONAL HEALTH/FITNESS AND A "FIT" ENVIRONMENT

Environmental Concepts		Physical Health/Fitness Concepts
1. Ecosystem	=	Our body
2. Carrying capacity	=	Physical fitness
3. Physical habitat	=	Lifestyle habits
4. Habitat characteristics	=	Health/fitness characteristics
*Adequate water	=	*Proper water and fluids
*Adequate food	=	*Proper nutrition
*Adequate shelter	=	*Maintenance of strength and flexibility
*Adequate space	=	*Maintenance of movement capability
*Adequate air quality	=	*Maintenance of cardiorespiratory endurance
5. Symbiotic relationships	=	Body health systems
* Plants, animals, and man	=	*Metabolic, nutrition, musculoskeletal, and cardiovascular systems

6. "Healthy" habitat management	=	Healthy lifestyle habits
7. Environment "stewardship" program	=	Fitness program as "stewardship" of the body
*Preservation and conservation	=	*Exercise, nutrition, rest
*Restoration	=	*Rehabilitation
*Personal decisions to help the ecosystem/habitat	=	*Personal decisions to maintain fitness

Culminating retreat activities consisted of providing model programs of exercise and nature activities together as stewardship projects for participants to apply within their schools or church grounds. Examples included building nature trails and par courses, developing habitat restoration areas, and erosion control mitigation.

Question #4: How Did It Work?
There was not any marketing or promotion of these programs. They were offered gratis based upon requests. Personal contacts with various Catholic dioceses culminated in requests for the Spirit, Mind and Body: A Faith Foundation for Fitness program for priests and seminarians. The CREATIO apostolate of the Christian Life Movement ran a retreat camp that served as a venue to offer the Stewardship of Nature and the Body program. Likewise they also ran parochial schools in the US, Peru, and Colombia that requested the Stewardship of Nature and the Body program.

Physically, the programs were delivered in a lecture setting with access to indoor or outdoor exercise facilities. In all the settings, it was always possible to provide the outdoor nature material in an outside setting that was adjacent.

Question #5: What Were the Results and Implications?
The Spirit, Mind and Body: A Faith Foundation for Fitness program was provided seven times, serving approximately 150 participants in

total. The Stewardship of Nature and the Body program was provided six times, including at two schools in Colombia, serving approximately one hundred adults and junior high students. As a follow-up to the program, several participants functioned as "parish stewardship leaders," and they aided six parish churches and schools to create nature stewardship projects on their grounds. While there was not any formal evaluation, the subjective feedback from participants was very positive.

Faith Implications

This section started out by noting that St. John Paul II was a role model for a faith-based active lifestyle and made many speeches on the value of exercise. He used his teaching authority to highlight the implications for physical activity to sustain both the body and the mind for all Christians. Here is a good example of his comments:

> Our body has a higher purpose than that of just providing the physical functions for our existence. Our body is not distinct from our spirit but is the vessel for it. One of our body's roles is to pay homage to God. As such we should be concerned with the well-being (stewardship) of our body. In an age that has witnessed the ever-increasing development of various forms of automation, especially in the workplace, reducing the use of physical activity, people need to find appropriate forms of physical exercise to restore a health balance of mind and body.

In turn, as was mentioned previously, St. John Paul II was also an advocate for caring for God's creation. In his 1990 World Day of Peace message, he expressed the need for stewardship of God's creation to the entire world. He said: "Human beings are appointed by God as stewards of the earth to cultivate and protect it. From this fact there comes what we might call their 'ecological vocation' which in our time has become more urgent than ever." In making the link between fitness and caring for the environment in the Stewardship of Nature and the

Body program, the concept of stewardship was broadened to encompass both a personal application (fitness) and a needed application of Christian service. That same theme of stewardship has other implications, as is reflected in Paul's first letter to the Corinthians (12:1–2), where he notes that the challenge of spiritual transformation involves showing proper respect for the body as part of that process: "I appeal to you therefore, brothers and sisters, by the mercies of God, to present your bodies as a living sacrifice, holy and acceptable to God, which is your spiritual worship. Do not be conformed to this world, but be transformed by renewing of your minds, so that you may discern what is the will of God—what is good and acceptable and perfect."

That spiritual transformation can be viewed as an element of Christian conversion. In that process, the final implication of faith-based physical fitness programs can be regarded in terms of the ultimate Christian purpose. As was stated in Ecclesiastes 12:13, "Fear God and keep his commandments, for this is the whole duty of man." The development and application of the stewardship ethic through physical activity can be a major means to fulfill our Christian duty.

In this chapter, programs were described that established the link between the fitness and faith missions. A healthy body is certainly the foundation for everything that life requires. Teaching tens of thousands of people across the globe to have faith in themselves as they remain mentally and physically vigilant for the unexpected was one of the most important missionary themes expressed in this memoir and history. However, it seems that far too many people fail to recognize that God helps those who truly help themselves. He needs for all to remain healthy and function properly so that one may not only help oneself, but so there is energy to do God's will and be of service to others in need.

CHAPTER 10
Final Thoughts

The previous chapters presented our experiences in the various Cooper Aerobics Center missionary outreaches. As mentioned, those efforts impacted a multitude of organizations and individuals. The underlying theme of those efforts was to change organizations to facilitate others (as well as the individuals themselves) to develop an exercise habit. While we explored in detail how it all worked in a variety of settings, a brief summary of the underlying process that, we believe, enabled our success can serve as a final explanation point to that effort.

AN UNDERLYING HABIT-CHANGE MODEL APPLIED

Changing any behavior is not easy. The data on adherence to exercise shows that 60–70 percent of nonexercisers who start a fitness program drop out within six months. It's a psychological issue, not a physiological problem. Various motivational strategies have been created over the years, from T-shirts rewards in fun runs to behavior contracting to alter habits. The behavior strategy that was defined though practical experience, which we then applied and taught, was, at one level, pretty basic.

Psychologist Robert Carkhuff, of the Human Technology group, many years ago defined a three-step helping process to change or modify negative habits: exploration, understanding, and action.

Exploration is the process of defining your current status (where you are). Understanding involves defining where you want or need to be. Action is defining how to get from where you are to where you want or need to be.

In terms of physical activity, the focus was on developing a positive exercise habit. We further defined that three-step process down into eight "core steps:"

Defining Where You Are

1. Health/medical screening to evaluate an individual's safety to engage in exercise.

2. Fitness assessment to define the individual's fitness level.

Defining Where You Want or Need to Be

3. Goal setting to establish "achievable" exercise and nutrition goals.

Defining How to Get from Where You Are to Where You Want or Need to Be

4. Exercise prescriptions to define detailed exercise and nutritional plans.

5. Definition of starter and safety programs to ensure a safe and gradual increase in activity.

6. Education to inform and answer the question, "Why exercise?"

7. Motivation strategies to reinforce activity efforts.

8. Feedback and follow-up strategies to monitor and reinforce one's exercise habits. Using the Cooper Aerobic point system was always a necessary monitoring ingredient of the exercise program.

Over the course of the many years of missionary efforts, we taught individuals to use that eight-step process to achieve and sustain a successful exercise habit. In turn, we worked with organizations to install a total exercise system that would encourage staff, patients, clients, and members to maintain their respective exercise programs. We did this by focusing on three main factors: people, programs, and organization.

The people factor was leadership. For the many programs in which we were responsible for training and overseeing organizational fitness leadership, it was imperative that the assigned fitness leaders were able to help participating individuals successfully navigate through the eight-step process. The program factor was assisting organizations and assuring them that only scientifically valid exercise and nutrition programming would be provided to their constituency. The organization factor was assistance in the design of the policies, procedures, and facilities that linked the leadership to the programs in a functional manner.

In summary, the exploration, understanding, and action phases and the eight-step process served as a model that many have been able to duplicate. Likewise, the focus on the organizational elements of people, program, and organization factors provided a blueprint for military and law enforcement agencies, schools, corporations, hospitals, and fitness centers to better serve their staffs and clienteles to develop and sustain the exercise habit.

UNDERLYING TRAITS FOR OUR WORK ETHIC

As mentioned in the introduction, this history and memoir is making a statement from three elderly fitness leaders (some would say "gym rats") who came together at a particular time and in a particular place with other like-minded professionals to work as a team for a common purpose. Many of the conclusions of and implications for those efforts have been explored in the previous chapters in detail and need not be replicated here. In reflecting upon the various "missionary" outreach programs described, we would rather define what we see as just a few simple but underlying and fundamental traits that we believe contributed to the eventual global impact of all those efforts.

A Catalyst

In many respects Dr. Cooper's vision and the Cooper Aerobics Center served as a catalyst for our efforts. He enabled us to expand and apply what we had learned before coming to the center to a much higher degree. A synergy was established that bore much fruit in the development of effective programs.

Leadership/Mentorship

The theme of the importance of leadership was taught and practiced throughout all the outreach programs. It was shared leadership, and from Dr. Cooper on down, we all served as mentors to each other. A big part of that leadership was the effect of staff modeling the active lifestyle.

Teamwork

There were no superstars among the staff, and we would fill in for each other when needed. Even though many had individual skill sets, the separate talents were blended into a cohesive whole that facilitated the accomplishment of many large-scale efforts.

The Sense of Mission Beyond Self

While the theme of a "mission" has been presented throughout this book, the missionary zeal was of a unique nature. The best way to describe it is that it was a sense that you were part of an organization and an effort that was bigger and more important than just you and your personal goals. It was the same kind of a subsuming of self to the larger group as seen in elite military units and championship athletic teams.

A Sense of Design
Many hours were spent planning for the various "missionary" outreach initiatives. However, there was always a sense that there was a design beyond our efforts that was not of our making. The way the professional staff came together from diverse backgrounds yet with a strong commonality of fitness and exercise as a core for our lives suggested a very unique "design." It's as if all our professional experiences had been preparing us to put it all together at the Cooper Aerobics Center at the same time to maximize our skills for the "missionary efforts." We believe that the design was God driven.

The Practice of the "Strenuous Life"—Endurance and Energy
Teddy Roosevelt preached the necessity of living the "strenuous life," and the name "aerobics" was applied to all our endeavors, which spoke to the importance of endurance. A high energy level was required at all times in delivering all the programs and projects. Staff modeled the "strenuous life" and were habitual exercisers. Most had competed in sports at the college level and above. As the staff entered into middle age and beyond, they continued their endurance activities, and most competed in triathlons, marathons, AAU Masters swimming, and other endurance events. Our energy was maintained throughout our tenures at the Cooper Aerobics Center.

Taking the Initiative
Dr. Cooper took the initiative in developing the aerobic point system and the Cooper Aerobics Center. It required a level of confidence and risk-taking that was necessary to demonstrate his belief that exercise is medicine. That same initiative was required in implementing the numerous "missionary" outreaches. There were many sideline critics who said we could not accomplish what we set out to do or attempted to discount the outcomes. All those criticisms were proven to be immaterial and irrelevant. In that context, the following quote by Teddy Roosevelt sums up our modus operandi to take a chance, to initiate, and to put all our efforts on the line:

It is not the critic who counts, not the one who points out how the strong man stumbled or how the doer of deeds might have done them better. The credit belongs to the man who is actually in the arena, whose face is marred with sweat and dust and blood; who strives valiantly; who errs and comes short again and again; who knows the great enthusiasms, the great devotions, and spends himself in a worthy cause; who, if he wins, knows the triumph of high achievement; and who, if he fails, at least fails while daring greatly, so that his place shall never be with those cold and timid souls who know neither victory nor defeat.

Authors' Histories

The staff of the Cooper Aerobics Center were exceptional individuals who exhibited a missionary zeal for their work. It would be impossible to explore the cause and impetus of where that kind of effort came from for each individual. However, we as the authors can provide as examples a glimpse into the origin of our personal motivation to be "fitness missionaries." For each of us, our lives have been defined by physical activity, exercise, and fitness. Therefore, as a final closing to this history and memoir, a brief summary of our personal stories and histories in becoming fitness missionaries is provided.

TOM'S STORY

Physical activity has defined my life in many diverse ways and contexts. It is a story of how the physical domain was a basic learning vehicle for my development from the younger years to my growing old age.

The Great Outdoors

Growing up in rural Indiana, we were constantly outside. Hunting, fishing, and hiking the woods and fields were almost daily activities, and we kids would ride bicycles for miles. We had a small Boy Scout troop that was always camping and doing nature conservation projects. All of us boys would do part-time seasonal farm work bailing hay and clearing fields and woods of slash. In high school I got a chain saw and started a firewood business clearing woods and cutting it up to sell and had a part-time job one summer as a tree feller. This all got me interested in forestry as a possible career, and it was my first major in college. While I never fully pursued it as a career, in my later years I have been able to return to that world as a volunteer nature interpretive ranger at Rocky Mountain National Park, as a volunteer master naturalist with Texas Parks and Wildlife, and as a hikemaster for the YMCA of the Rockies. In all these efforts, I led hikes into the mountains or prairies.

I have been very fortunate to have traveled the world, and whether for work or pleasure, I have taken advantage of opportunities to experience the variety of ecosystems and natural life our world offers. Hiking days were always part of the itinerary. Whether in the Alps, the Andes, the Rockies, the Smokies, jungles, the Pacific islands, or the deserts of the Middle East, these experiences reinforced that we are made to move and to move in our outdoor environment. It is our natural gymnasium and running track.

A further involvement in nature was the recognition of the need for a faith-based commitment to our environment and our human responsibility as caretakers of God's creation. That recognition led to my developing the religious retreat on a faith-based ethic, Stewardship of Nature and the Body, that was previously mentioned.

Movement outdoors is not only a pleasant physical experience, but upon reflection, it also serves as a mental health outlet. Whenever I am feeling depressed or having to make a decision, going for a walk or a hike outside clears my mind, gives me a sense of balance about things, and just makes me feel good. It allows one to experience a commonality with all of nature and God's creation. The importance of outdoor activities as a vehicle for exercise and movement was later incorporated into some of the Cooper Institute Continuing Education curriculum.

My love of the outdoors has been passed on to my family, kids, and grandkids to the point where my kids even got degrees in parks and recreation. Camping, backpacking, or hiking have been the family gathering activity norms—summer or winter.

Sports and Exercise

In the 1960s there was a TV show called *The Wide World of Sports* which highlighted a variety of athletic events. In many respects that sums up the diversity of sports and physical activity that I have experienced over the years. Baseball was the first sport in my early years. I played on some of the first Little League baseball teams and later for my high school and American Legion baseball teams. As an extension to baseball, in later years into my late thirties and early forties, I played fast-pitch softball until it lost popularity with men to the slow-pitch game.

My favorite sport was football; I played as a lineman. I played throughout high school; two years in college (Michigan Tech and Ball State), earning a partial scholarship; and a year of service ball in the army. Following those years, I played on some recreational flag football teams into my midthirties. In college, I also threw the discus and javelin on the track team and later on, after college, threw one summer for an AAU amateur team.

Growing up in Indiana, I played basketball, but it wasn't my favorite winter sport. During my teen years, I played in an ice hockey league and wrestled for the local YMCA team. It was at the Y that I picked up handball, which I eventually played into the 1990s until it died out, to be replaced by racquetball, which, as a handball purist, I didn't like. The only racket sport I did play was tennis and, in my forties and fifties, I played in a doubles league but gave it up after some injuries.

I started working out for fitness in junior high school, initially by doing just push-ups and sit-ups and then adding other exercises, including resistance weight training and endurance work. I have practiced that basic daily routine for almost seventy years. I got into running when the Cooper Aerobics program became popular and did several 10K races. Modifications were made (adding lap swimming and biking) which got me involved in doing some mini-triathlons in my forties. Throughout it all, a daily workout became a sold habit of my life. The self-discipline to stick with anything that must be applied in any domain or situation was learned through this process. It is a trait that I passed on to others.

n some of the program applications made at the Cooper Aerobics Center years later.

Many of my other physical activities were related to my exercise habits and routines. As I aged into my fifties, I was fortunate to be able to spend many months of the year in Colorado, so at a late age, I picked up skiing, preferring cross-country to downhill. Due to injuries, those had to be dropped, and now the winter activity is snowshoeing. Since having to give up running many years ago, daily walking, stationary cycling, and mountain hiking have been a major aerobic physical activity. A related activity I got involved in was orienteering with a map and compass and, for several years, as a volunteer ranger, teaching it as a visitor program in Rocky Mountain National Park.

I learned many lessons from sustaining a lifetime habit of exercise. It isn't so much about competition or being locked into only one sport or activity but about being committed to the overall habit of movement. In my case, adjustments had to be made many times over the years to a different activity or modified exercise because of injuries and age. Throughout it all, the desire to keep moving and exercising regardless of mode of activity was supreme. A lot of things happen when one exercises—biologically, physically, and psychologically—all of them good. These experiences of my life have confirmed the value of movement and exercise.

As with the outdoors, the love of sports and physical activity has been passed on to my family. My wife was a really good tennis player until injuries sidelined her. Family games and activities of a physical nature are a staple of our get-togethers. A yearly event is the "Gorilla Olympics," whereby I design an obstacle course around our mountain home with fitness tests as well. My kids and grandkids participate in a variety of sports, and their activity level could be described as being human tornadoes."

Foundations for a Career in Physical Activity

The trajectory of my professional career in physical fitness and activity was not a direct path and took many twists and turns before culminating in being part of the Cooper Aerobics Center "missionary team." There were many diversions, and they all provided learning experiences that contributed lessons that were later applied to the Cooper Aerobics Center mission.

After high school graduation, I started my first real full-time jobs: heavy construction (road and pipeline) for four summers and one full year. In the 1960s, they were high-paying jobs with lots of overtime. Coupled with GI Bill payments of $155 a month, a small athletic scholarship, and Veterans Administration internships, those jobs paid for all eight years of eventual undergraduate and graduate education later on, which was important since my folks couldn't afford to send me to college. It was hard work from sunup to sundown. It was the first time I recognized that fitness is "job related," which became one of the areas of programming at the Cooper Aerobics Center to assist others in increasing their job-related fitness.

After two years of college, education was put on hold because I didn't know what I wanted in a career, so I joined the US Army. I volunteered as a paratrooper with the elite 82nd Airborne Division and was selected to be trained as a military policeman (MP). The 82nd Airborne Military Police detachment prided itself in being the most fit and toughest MP outfit in the army, and because of that we were the only MP unit in the army that didn't need to carry clubs.

The 82nd Airborne then (1960s) and now is viewed as America's "911" rapid-response team. Division elements were on two- to twenty-four-hour alerts to go anywhere in the world. Physical readiness (fitness) was a necessity to complete a multitude of missions that would require not only immediate deployment but then require jumping into often difficult terrain with sustained long-range patrols lasting several days without any support or replacements. The lessons of the necessity of physical readiness (fitness) were quickly learned as also critical for survival to meet the mission demands, to not let your team down, and to keep up, as well as being a key factor for survival if wounded or injured. Because of the unique missions assigned to Airborne, Ranger, and Special Forces units, physical fitness is highly regarded and demanded in these units.

An example is seen in this sentence of the "Airborne Creed" one had to memorize in jump school: "I realize that a parachutist is not merely a soldier who arrives by parachute to fight but is an elite shock-trooper and that his country expects him to march farther and faster than any other soldier."

Daily intense physical training was the norm; we used to say that "we do more before 7:00 a.m. than most people do in a full day," and I often led the daily PT sessions. The physical domain was the key vehicle to train troopers into having a can-do ethic, which is expressed in the Airborne motto. There are two elements to that motto that are said every time a current or former paratrooper greets or communicates with one another. One says "Airborne," and the response is "All the way." That motto has significant meaning. "All the way" reflects an attitude that means you will not shirk your duty, you will do whatever has to be done to accomplish the mission, you will go the extra mile, and you will never give up. The often-used cliché "110 percent" is expected as the norm.

As a personal sidenote, there is a camaraderie and a fraternal nature to having been a paratrooper that stays with you the rest of your life and even crosses international boundaries. A key element is the shared intense physical activity and fitness that all paratroopers throughout the world have a common pride in. Throughout my life and career, there have been numerous occasions to casually meet and socialize with veteran paratroopers. There is an instant bond, relationship, and sense of brotherhood, often to the extent that I have had many free beers. It is impossible to fully explain all this except to repeat what one old paratrooper said to me: "We made a statement that will live with us forever." In many respects, when I look at what would occur later on at the Cooper Aerobics Center, all of that could be considered a similar making of a significant statement.

The significance of these service experiences cannot be understated. They not only fit quite naturally into my existing physical nature, but they facilitated another level of commitment necessary in working toward a mission with a team in a variety of other domains. Having that "all the way" attitude was a key trait for accomplishing various Cooper

155

Aerobics Center missions in later years. It also provided an important background for when we were involved in working with the army's Physical Readiness program in the 1980s.

Upon leaving the army, I went back to college but, after a year, got expelled. I was always a bit rowdy, and I came out of the service somewhat rough around the edges. I worked heavy construction on a pipeline for a year and, during that time, started dating and got engaged to my wife, Gretchen. Her influence helped to "civilize the young savage" and motivated me to go back to college. As a consequence, I finally got a BS degree, then went on to get graduate degrees (MS in exercise science, PhD in psychology).

A Diverse Career in Physical Fitness and Activity

I have been a member of the YMCA for most of my life, and in the last year of graduate school, I worked as an assistant YMCA camp director. As a follow-up, I was recruited to be a YMCA director in Pittsburgh. It was there that I learned the YMCA fitness model and group exercise leadership techniques that were applied years later in some of the Cooper Aerobics Center programs.

Following the YMCA experience, a few years were spent in rehabilitation research and academic settings (University of Arkansas, Louisiana State University) implementing exercise programs for mentally disturbed and substance-abusing youth and young adults. One of the most challenging efforts was leading a group of nineteen teenage drug users on a two-and-a-half-week wilderness survival backpacking trek through the Ozark Mountains of Arkansas. The good Lord was looking out for us, and there were no major injuries or snake bites. Evaluations of these programs showed that such exercise and physical experiences had significant effects on lowering substance abuse with improved mental health. These efforts were an example of applying and transferring what I had learned through past military and physical training experiences. That model of transferring what was learned to other application areas became a template for many of the future efforts in youth programming that occurred years later at the Cooper Aerobics Center.

Because of my background as a military policeman, academic training as a psychologist, and youth work, I applied for and was selected to be a police psychologist with the Dallas Police Department (DPD). My major responsibility was to supervise a unit of twelve in the Youth Division and work with arrested youth. Physical fitness activities were a major component used to teach responsibility and self-discipline. It was a very successful program, and we were able to significantly reduce the rearrest rate of thousands of youth. My right and left arms, Hadley Williams and Alex Douds were significant contributors to that success. That experience, along with the previous youth exercise programs, provided a real sense of mission to use exercise to help at-risk youth in later efforts at the Cooper Aerobics Center.

A collateral duty with the DPD was to lead exercise classes as an in-service fitness program for officers, and that duty lead me into contact, for the first time, with the Cooper Aerobics Center. The Cooper Institute along with the DPD obtained a grant from the International Association of Chiefs of Police (IACP) to assess the need for and design training regimens for police fitness. I was tasked with being a liaison to Dr. Mike Pollack and Dr. Larry Gettman, who headed up the Exercise Physiology Lab for the institute at that time. As a follow-up to that study, the three of us conduced nationwide seminars for the IACP to inform police departments of the findings. That started a relationship between the IACP, the Cooper Aerobics Center, and me that facilitated many cooperative efforts and courses for many years.

A few years later, while a training director at the Kentucky Department of Justice, I developed a police fitness leader training course. That course would serve, later on, as the model for not only law enforcement fitness leaders, but for all fitness leader courses through the Cooper Aerobics Center. At the same time, the President's Council on Physical Fitness and Sports was making efforts to address public safety fitness (police and fire), and I was asked to be the council's consultant in this area. As consequence, I worked with them to make recommendations and to teach at their regional clinics on that topic. As with the IACP, a relationship was established that was carried on later at the Cooper Aerobics Center for many cooperative national fitness initiatives.

Onward to the Cooper Aerobics Center

In 1979, Dr. Cooper wanted to establish a continuing education division so that courses could be provided through the center as part of his total mission. Larry Gettman (whom I had worked with a few years previous with the IACP project) contacted me, and I was hired for that position. It was an opportunity to apply and grow my diverse personal and professional experiences in exercise and fitness to a whole other level. After several years at the Cooper Aerobics Center, I was honored to receive the Healthy American Fitness Leader Award as one of the top 10 Fitness Leaders in America and I accepted it on behalf of the CI staff. While an individual can make a difference, I recognized that if he is part of a larger team effort, the impact becomes exponential to go beyond individual concerns and aspirations to that which could be bigger and more powerful. It is a "we" effort, not a "me" effort.

A Final Conclusion

A final refection on a life of physical activity and movement is that I believe there was a design to it all. God has a plan for us, but we don't always realize it. As I look back, it is now apparent that all my somewhat haphazard experiences were preparing me to "put it all together" for the Cooper Aerobics Center missionary efforts.

A major part of God's plan for was for me to marry Gretchen. Since graduate school, she has been my patient mentor, adviser, sounding board, and leveler. She has taught me that it isn't about the end result but about the journey, and I could never have pursued the journey without her.

ROGER'S STORY

Family

was born in 1940 as the second son of four brothers. Our address was 63 Elm Street, London, Ohio. We continued to live at this address until we brothers got married and moved into our own family homes. Our mother, Dorothea, would prove to be nothing less than one of God's angels sent directly from heaven. This magnificent lady in 1962 became honored as Ohio's Mother of the Year along with John Glenn's mother.

My early childhood memories were full of love, faith, sacrifice, hard work, selflessness, and a family working together in order to survive. Our father made the choice to pursue his life elsewhere and left our mother with four sons ages eleven, eight, seven, and six. In spite of this, our mother emerged as an absolute pillar of Christian strength and unshakable faith. It was due to our mother's pure willpower that she was able to move our lives forward against impossible odds. To say that our family life was a constant struggle for survival is definitely an understatement. My three brothers and I quickly learned how to work as a team if we were to survive. This was my very first observation, experience, and understanding of how a team has to work together if they are to be successful. This concept of team would eventually lead me to the great missionary team at the Cooper Aerobic Center.

As I look back, it was family that became the undeniable rock of importance in my life. Of all the various teams that I have served, the "family team" far exceeds in overall importance any other team which I have been a part of. It has been said that most of our personality is developed by the age of five to six. Therefore, it becomes essentially important to be sure that the concepts of love, respect, discipline, making choices, educational growth, and consequences are imbedded within our children as early as possible. These life values were deeply imbedded within each of us four brothers by the way we lived.

The core element for our family was physical activity. Fitness was a necessity in order to meet the demanding day-to-day schedule. My wife and I have always remained very active. We have taught exercise classes for over twenty-five years together, in addition to running numerous 10K races and one marathon. Besides my brothers, the love of athletics and sports has been passed down to our children and grandchildren. My oldest son, Randy, was a very successful high school football player and later achieved success as a competitive bodybuilder. My daughter, Lisa, has participated in and led aerobic fitness classes and competed in road races ranging from 10K to half marathon. As a mother she is now very active in her walking program. My second son, Shawn, became a three-sport athlete in high school and later became the twelfth man on the Texas A&M football team. He has competed in numerous road races from 10K to marathon and competed in the triathlon. My youngest son, Lance, was a very successful high school baseball player and later became a distance runner, winning many road races from 10Ks to marathons. One of his goals is to qualify for the Boston Marathon. At the age of three, he actually competed in his first 5K race, running beside his mom and finishing first in his age group. We are truly blessed that all six grandchildren—Reece, Brooke, Ally, Heidi, Landry, and Cooper—are engaged in exercise and activities that are fun and challenging. I guess you could say that exercise "runs in the family"!

One of the most memorable, challenging, and rewarding fitness events that my children and I competed in together was on my sixtieth birthday. As my birthday present, we entered a twenty-four-hour wilderness eco-adventure race. This very demanding course consisted of a variety of physical and mental adventures in the mountains of south Texas. Our team average age was the oldest in the competition. However, we actually finished in eighth place out of forty-six teams.

Childhood Years

We lived in a duplex with three rooms, one small bathroom, and two upstairs bedrooms. In the very cold winters, we heated our entire house by a small gas heater in the bathroom and one in the front room. There was no heat in the two upstairs bedrooms. The gas stove oven door was left open at night so the heat could go upstairs by the stairway. We had one very small bathroom, which required our mother keeping the order of bathing up to date. Whoever was the last one in had mostly really dirty water! I did not take my first shower until I was in high school, which was after PE class.

As we brothers grew up, we had a paper route from the age of seven. This required getting out of bed by 5:30 AM every morning except Sunday. One hour to pass our papers, come home and get ready for school by 8: 00 AM. We each held this job until our teens when we started painting houses for our uncles, Oscar and Logan Gibson. Our summer schedules were full of doing almost everything outside. We were always competing as teams. We spent a lot of time at the local creek swimming and fishing, looking for frogs and snakes, or playing games such as red rover, allie allie in free, kick the can, and hide and seek in the summer and going sledding, ice skating, and just playing in the snow during the winter. No one had much money. We had our paper route money and would find pop bottles at the fairgrounds, which were worth two cents each for their deposit. That was about all the money we ever had. We would stand at the fence and watch all of our friends as they were swimming because we could not afford to go swimming, which was about ten cents each visit to the pool. Since we did not have the money to go swimming on those very hot days at the London Swimming Pool, we went to the creek to cool off. Later, during our high school years, Bob, Gary, Dick, and I were lifeguards.

As we reached the ages of seven and eight, our entire summer day was spent playing baseball from dawn to dark. In the fall, it was playing football either in the pasture across the street from our house or in our friend Will Pratt's side yard. In the winter it was basketball outside, even in the snow; and in the spring it was competitive track meets held in the vacant lot at the corner. We definitely became creative in order to find games to play that had some kind of scoring and competition attached. I would be remiss if I did not mention the vital role our grandparents played in our lives. Proctor & Ollie Gibson and Ben & Leona Reynolds were the most loving and caring grandparents we brothers could have ever asked for. It is my prayer that my brothers and I also serve our grandchildren as similar role models.

Sports and Athletics

The Reynolds brothers became known in our hometown and in many of the surrounding towns as the upcoming athletes of the future. During Little League baseball, Gary, Dick, and I all led the league in home runs each year. Our teams also won the championship every year. The three of us each hit eleven home runs in one season. We had similar success playing in the Babe Ruth League and later with the American Legion baseball team. Competing in sports at such an early age was definitely another lesson in how to play together as a team and what position was best for each of us.

During high school, I began to excel in all sports. I became Central Ohio's Player of the Year in football and was selected to the all-conference teams in football, basketball, and baseball during my junior and senior years. As a senior, I was awarded our high school's Most Outstanding Athlete of the Year award, which my two younger brothers, Gary and Dick, also won their senior years. I was later inducted into the LHS Athletic Hall of Fame. Our football and basketball teams won the league championships during my junior and senior years. My high school years were the very best I could have ever asked for, including being elected our senior class president. My classmates of 1959 still remain some of my most cherished friends.

My athletic career continued into college as I received several major college football scholarship offers. After visiting several of these schools, I decided to stay close to home and accepted a football scholarship from Bowling Green State University (BGSU) in Bowling Green, Ohio. During my four years at BGSU, we won three Mid-American Conference Championships and won the NCAA Small College Football National Championship in 1959. While on those BGSU teams, I was ranked as the number-two best kick-off returner in the NCAA, was the fourth-best receiver in the MAC, and was subsequently selected as a member of the All Mid-American Football Team. Those recognitions led to being inducted into the BGSU Athletic Hall of Fame and opened the door for a career in the NFL.

In the spring of my senior year, I was recruited to sign an NFL contract with the New York Giants. My childhood dream of playing professional football was actually unfolding into reality. The New York Giants were Eastern Division Champion in 1961–62, and, because of their experienced returning players, were preseason picks to win the 1963 World Championship (which is now called the Super Bowl). Facing almost impossible odds of making this outstanding player roster (in addition to the list of 1963 high-profile drafted players from across the nation), my work was certainly cut out for me.

In preparation for my first NFL training camp, I endured an extremely demanding and exhaustive winter and summer workout schedule. My fitness level was at its highest point in my life. My conditioning program had given me a definite edge on my competing receivers. I was recovering faster and running more routes than any of my competitors. Additionally, I would stay after practice and run routes with Frank Gifford or our all-pro quarterback Y.A. Tittle when other receivers went into shower because they were too tired. It all paid off in that in my very first game as a rookie against the Chicago Bears, I caught three passes for seventy-nine yards and was selected as the most outstanding offensive player of the game.

My professional football career continued for three good years with the New York Giants. However, injuries became more and more of a problem throughout my career, and I was traded to the Atlanta Falcons for two years, then the Cincinnati Bengals, where I ended my professional career. At Cincinnati, my receiver coach was Bill Walsh (later the head coach of the 49ers), and our head coach was Paul Brown. Those were two of the most successful coaches in the history of the NFL and were regarded as two of the greatest minds in the game. That season was the absolute greatest experience of my career, and what I learned from them was later applied when I got into coaching.

Major injuries became a constant threat to my career. It is well understood that a professional athlete's greatest fear is an injury or injuries that continue. We all had to play hurt at some time, but when the hurt effects performance, it is serious. My career ended with a fractured nose injury. It seemed to put everything in proper perspective as it does for every professional athlete, and that is, "It is time to seek employment elsewhere."

Military Athletics and Fitness
I graduated from Bowling Green State University as a Distinguished Military Student in the army ROTC program and was eventually ordered to report for active duty. Upon reporting for active duty at Ft. Benning, Georgia, and completing the US Army Basic Officer Training School, I was assigned to serve as the Ft. Benning Sports and Athletic Officer, responsible for physical training and the Ft. Benning Sports Program, consisting of forty-five thousand troops. I headed up this office with a staff of ten NCOs and about twenty enlisted men. It was while serving my military duty that I learned another valuable lesson about what a team means to a combat unit. Everyone is totally committed to absolutely doing their assigned job. It is about the importance of the chain of command. It was here that I first saw the necessity of physical fitness for 24-7 combat readiness. Once the Infantry School instructors discovered I had played in the NFL, I was assigned temporary duty to play on the Ft. Benning football team. I took great pride in being one of the captains of the Ft. Benning Doughboy football team. We were undefeated with a record of 14-0 and finished the season by winning the Military Missile Bowl Championship.

Coaching and Teaching
Following my military service, I accepted a position to attend Western Michigan University on a graduate assistantship and was assigned to coach the varsity football receivers, teach physical education classes, and attend graduate school full time. It was a very demanding schedule, but I finished with honors grades and received my master's degree in exercise science. I had been a follower of Dr. Cooper's aerobic point program since 1968, and I requested that Dr. Cooper serve as my master's thesis adviser. My thesis concerned the application of aerobic points as a system to measure exercise training effects and thereby predict

which division-one varsity sport produces the best all-around-fitness athlete. Dr. Cooper provided me specific direction on establishing my design for proper testing.

Following my graduate work, I was recruited by several high schools to become their head football coach. After much travel and investigating various schools, I accepted the position at Penn High School in Mishawaka, Indiana, a very large high school that had won the Northern Indiana Conference All-Sports Award for the previous three years but was not successful in football. I led a coaching staff consisting of fifteen coaches covering two middle schools and a junior varsity and varsity program. As with everything in my life, a total team effort was required. The total commitment of players and coaches during the years of 1971-73 were the early building foundation years for one of the most successful high school football programs in Indiana. Following my coaching and teaching at Penn, I returned to coaching at Western Michigan University.

As I returned to my career path pursuing NCAA division-one teaching and coaching, I became very interested in the growing adult exercise movement and, in particular, the work that Dr. Kenneth Cooper was doing in promoting aerobics. Dr. Cooper's work had been very personal and important to me, as I had used his aerobic point system while training as a professional athlete. I was fascinated with the structure and simplicity of his system. I loved university-level teaching and coaching but was beginning to visualize a somewhat different future using the application of aerobic exercise for many other situations. I truly sensed a divine calling for me to follow a new career path and focus on my passion to help adults and children become more physically fit. At WMU, while I was tasked with managing the off-season workout program for our players, Annette (my wife), noticed an ad in her college physical education bulletin that was of significant interest to me. A professional organization was looking for experienced PE teachers and/or athletic coaches with experience in public speaking. This national organization was in the process of recruiting a team of professionals who would serve on the staff of a National Fitness Motivation Organization. Joining that organization functioned as the springboard for my fitness career.

Moving Into a Career in Fitness

During the following several years, I was committed to exploring various ways in which my passion for exercise and fitness could become a fruitful career. It seemed to me that a logical place to reach large numbers of potential clients would be at the place where they were working. I needed a unique marketing strategy to promote my idea of what I referred to as a company-based fitness program. Using previous contacts from my career, I began public speaking throughout Indiana, motivating people on the value and effect of proper exercise. My initial presentations were delivered to civic groups such as Rotary Clubs, Lyon Clubs, and Chamber of Commerce groups throughout the Midwest. Many of these club members represented local businesses, and my hope was that they would take my message back to their management and seek a follow-up meeting with me to discuss what I could do to help them. Obviously, my end goal was to have their business consider providing a fitness program for their management and/or employees.

A major factor that dramatically aided my progress was when Indiana Senator Richard Lugar contacted me to discuss his support of what I was doing and what I could do in the future to have a positive impact on health and fitness throughout the state. Senator Lugar was a longtime Cooper Clinic patient of Dr. Cooper's and became one of my most supportive celebrities for many years. He opened many valuable doors for me as my presentations became increasingly requested throughout the Midwest.

Implementing Corporate Fitness Programs

In response to the many requests following my presentations, I began to structure a workplace fitness program and developed the plan for how I would implement it in the business setting. I was able to sell this program to the leaders in business and industry throughout the Michiana area where we lived. After working on the various components of this program, I settled on a basic twelve-week fitness program very similar to the one I would later design for the DISD on teacher fitness and stress management detailed in chapter 6 of this book.

Shortly after creating the program design, I met with Barry S. Brown, PhD, who was chair of the Exercise Physiology Department at the University of Arkansas. He was also working with the National Fitness Motivation Organization at this time. Following our meeting, we agreed to join forces in developing a new business organization. The new business would be named Human Performance Systems (HPS). The business manager and vice president would be Mr. Larry Slamons, another staff member from the University of Arkansas. Our vice president and medical director would be Dr. James McNair from Little Rock, Arkansas, and director of nutrition would be Richard Lewis, PhD. Barry would serve as our president, and I would serve as vice president and director of all programs. We would subcontract all necessary assistance as we went forward. Barry brought his graduate and postgraduate students who indicated an interest in corporate fitness into our organization as part-time staff. Additionally, he assumed the responsibility of identifying, recruiting, and training all medical personnel that were needed to deliver our programs. Our national office would be located in South Bend, Indiana, and I would work out of that office, with Mrs. Judy Kenna serving as my executive secretary, bookkeeper, and scheduling coordinator. She was perfect for this very important position.

Within two years, we had delivered our programs to over eighteen clients, including large corporations, companies, small businesses, fire and police departments, Indiana State Police, Indiana National Guard, financial institutions, and others. As our business increased, so did the need for additional offices to be located where our future work was taking us. The Chicago market became our immediate focus. Eventually, all of northern Illinois, Indiana, and southern Michigan and Ohio became our markets. A second office was established in the Downtown Court Club located in downtown Chicago. Our first and most successful large corporate fitness program was delivered to the World Corporate Offices of Encyclopedia Britannica. The success of that program became the catalyst that successfully promoted our program throughout the Midwest.

In 1978, our program was selected as the ACSM Midwest Chapter Corporate Fitness Program of the Year, and in 1980, I was chosen as a finalist in the selection of National Corporate Fitness Director of the Year by the national governing body titled American Association of Fitness Directors in Business and Industry.

Onward to the Cooper Aerobics Center

Throughout those years, I continued to provide Dr. Cooper with our program results, details, and research data. He was always supportive and encouraging of my work. The next and final step in my passionate fitness career occurred when I was asked to join the Cooper Aerobics Center Staff. All the aforementioned experiences provided a foundation, especially for the concept of teamwork, that I was able to bring to bear at the Cooper Aerobics Center. My dream of working with Dr. Cooper at his famous complex was actually becoming a reality.

The Faith, Fitness, and Teamwork Connection

Much of my life could be defined as one dictated by physical activity/ fitness, my faith, and the concept of "team." The interrelationship of those elements of my being was significantly brought home when at the age of seventy, I faced a series of health crises. I needed to have a biopsy of a growth on my leg and went to my surgeon's office for what I assumed would be positive results. However, the alarming news came out of the blue when he said to me, "Roger, I believe you have something more serious than you thought." Follow-up surgery to remove the tumor revealed the seriousness of my situation. The tumor was, in fact, malignant, and the complete diagnosis confirmed that it was a stage three non-Hodgkin's lymphoma blood cancer. Little did I know that this would be the beginning of a ten-year battle.

The first course of treatment was somewhat tolerable (chemo through infusion therapy for twelve weeks). However, as any cancer patient will tell you, chemo takes almost all your energy and your taste and causes increasing nausea. Following this first round of treatment, I started to feel better, and I returned to my work, which included work-related travel. It was about that time when the cancer struck again. It was necessary for me to undergo another twelve-week chemo infusion reatment and add additional drugs to the treatment. My energy level and overall function was reaching a dangerous overall health condition. A team of stem cell surgeons were brought in to assess my condition. It was determined that a stem cell transplant was the only recourse to overcome the disease.

The stem cell transplant process was a daunting thirty-day hospital isolation ordeal whereby my immune system would be brought down to literally zero. The process began with a seven-day, 24-7 infusion of the strongest chemo to reduce my immune system to nothing. Prior to my admittance, it was determined that my personal six thousand stem cells were free of cancer and therefore could be harvested and reinfused into my body. The infused healthy stem cells basically gave me a new life. I will never forget that day when my wife and family, along with our family minister, Clayton Oliphint, offered a prayer over the six thousand stem cells that were in IV bags beside me. As these six thousand stem cells were infused into my body, the surgeon told me they knew exactly where to go and what to do, and I said, "Praise the Lord."

Through it all, my energy was totally sapped, and I lost more than forty pounds. It literally took all my strength just to get out of bed. Sometime during these thirty days, I asked my doctors if they could put a stationary bike in my room. In my condition of unbelievable weakness, everyone thought I had finally lost my mind. However, by just sitting on the bike, my mind was visualizing another place in another time. I could mentally visualize riding on my bike in earlier years out in the country where the scene was very peaceful. I was actually in my own little world visualizing, happy, and praying. At one time while I was sitting on my bike and pedaling about once or twice a minute, Lisa, who was watching with Annette said, "If Dad goes any slower, he's gonna fall off!"

Family, friends, and Dr. Cooper visited regularly and gave me tremendous encouragement, which really helped get me started on the road to recovery. It started with little five- to ten-minute walks around the room and then the ward floor. Tom would come up to visit and walk with me almost every day. We would walk the hall together as we laughed a little and shared happier times. Finally, I was released five days earlier than predicted. Four months after I was released, the hospital library was divided into a fitness room, which included two indoor bikes!

Unfortunately, cancer has a way of not letting you go without a fight. Over the next few years, my cancer recovery was threatened by three malignant melanoma surgeries, followed by a serious urinary tract infection that sent me back into the hospital for another surgery. It was during these really tough years that my life was continually at risk and my mind was having a very difficult time processing everything I was going through. My days were filled with doctor appointments, and depression started to set in, and it slowly became very serious. For the first time I could ever remember, I had no desire to exercise; even walking around the block was out of the question. Finally, Dr. Boyd Lyles, my physician and personal friend for over thirty years, referred me to a psychiatrist and depression therapist. Following two hospital admissions and a newly developed depression treatment involving transcranial magnetic brain stimulation (TMS), I was finally ready to resume my life. I had lost a total of fifty-one pounds during the entire experience. I started to get back to religiously working out, which became the key to my total recovery and beyond.

From my initial diagnosis of cancer, I continuously fought for my life through what seemed to be a never-ending mental and physical battle. Finally, in February 2021, Dr. Barry Brooks, my fantastic oncologist from the beginning, officially declared me clear from cancer! I had regained my weight and precancer fitness through my devoted exercise program, which consisted of two hours per workout, six days a week. Dr. Cooper always maintained that "exercise is medicine," and I certainly proved him right. The doctors and medical experts all claimed that my recovery and healing was truly a miracle. Yes, I also believe it was indeed a miracle. However, this miracle was a direct result of a "supreme team victory" that can be attributed to my medical team, my family team, my praying team of friends, and finally my faith team, confirmed by my complete and total trust in God Almighty as our team captain! Our team scripture reads, "I can do all things through Christ who strengthens me" (Philippians 4:13).

JOHN'S STORY

Have you ever said to yourself or to others in your presence, "I think there is something providential in that?" Meaning that whatever the event, it was intended and possibly blessed by God. Seeking an answer to this question requires us to carefully identify and clarify what we believe and see if we have made our actions consistent with our beliefs.

We know that what we believe in is generally influenced by our background, our experience, our DNA, and our environment. Can you tell what a person believes by observation and close association? My answer to that question is a resounding yes. I believe in God as my creator and in Jesus Christ as my redeemer. I believe in my country, its strength, its compassion, and its exceptionalism in spite of its flaws. I believe in hard work or giving all you've got for the greater good, in perseverance, in a balance between competition and cooperation, in humility, in serving, and in loving your neighbor as yourself, which bears out the Golden Rule.

Our beliefs and attitudes are shaped early in life and so often are determine the choices we make. We don't have much choice in the circumstances into which we are born. As we mature, we are afforded the opportunity to make more of our own choices. If you are a student of history, you might think of 1929, the year I was born, as a year of unfortunate circumstances. Actually, it was many years of unfortunate circumstances, for the Great Depression, which began in 1929 and lasted until the late 1930s, was followed by World War II, which lasted until the mid-1940s. So how did ninety-one years shape those beliefs, and what purpose was served in their accumulation?

Learning From Deprivation

The early years of my life were marked by what today would be called deprivation: no electricity; no running water indoors, and consequently no indoor plumbing; three rooms for six people. The main room was the kitchen, dining room, living room, and yes, bathroom, where you bathed in a number three washtub. A wood (or coal) stove provided warmth, but cooking was done on the two-burner kerosene (or coal oil) stove.

The toilet was the outhouse. If you have used a port-a-potty recently, you may think that's not too bad; imagine using one for twenty years of your life. The other two rooms were bedrooms with no heat, and the back porch was screened in to be used as a sleeping porch. No central heat; no problem. There were always plenty of quilts and blankets and lots of flannel pajamas to keep us toasty.

No air conditioning; no problem. Those hot summer days and nights found all of our windows up and doors wide open. The windows were screened to keep out the bugs and varmints and were propped open with a "window stick," a common and well-known term in those days. Window sticks were not store bought but were usually sawed-off mop or broom handles. Screen doors were in front of the wooden doors and were secured by a simple hook-and-eye latch. No family car; no telephone. Bed clothes and heavy work clothes, like overalls, were washed in a big iron washpot. Wood or coal provided the heat for boiling the water. Lighter clothing was washed on a washboard (rub board) in a number three washtub. Everything was hung on the clothesline to dry.

Homework was done by a kerosene lamp. When I was about ten, electricity came to the county, so we bought a small Stewart-Warner radio on which we listened to some of the old programs: Fibber McGee and Molly, Amos N' Andy, Jack Benny—and lots of static. If you did not experience those circumstances, you wouldn't understand; you had to have been there.

My mom, Jewell, was a master seamstress who made almost all of our clothes: underwear out of flour sacks, shirts, blouses, short pants, knickers, footie pajamas, and dresses for sis. Shoes, socks, and long pants were about the only things we bought. She was also an excellent barber; my first "store-bought" haircut was at the age of fifteen. We felt stretched a little once in a while, but we didn't feel poor.

Deprivation was not abject poverty. We had just enough money to make ends meet. We had a roof over our heads, clean clothes to wear, and enough food to eat. We had two acres of garden, so we had fresh vegetables and fruits through the spring and summer, and Mom and Grandma canned enough food to last through most of the winter.

Having chickens meant we had plenty of eggs...and fried chicken for dinner almost every Sunday. Ol' Blackie provided us with lots of milk and butter. I'm sure you know how milk to butter happens. Brown bag school lunches might be potted meat sandwiches and an apple or orange. Vienna sausage and Spam were a treat. Bread was twelve cents a loaf, and flour, corn meal, salt, and sugar were dirt cheap; it didn't take a lot of money to live. Although it was no consolation, a very large percentage of the population endured the same set of circumstances.

In those early days, there was not much geographic or social mobility. If you were born in a small town, you were raised by a small town, and your expectation was to die in that small town. Families were very close, and many times lived together for financial stability and mutual support. There were parents, grandparents, aunts, uncles, and cousins, all of whom were your advocates. In small towns like West, Texas, where I was born, everyone knew everyone, so there was lots of community advocacy.

The first five years of my life, my dad, my mom, my sis, and I lived with my paternal grandparents, my favorite uncle, and two teenage boy cousins. It worked out well. Everyone worked hard and lived by the rules, so there was little time for disagreements or friction. When I was five, the four of us moved to live with my widowed maternal grandmother and my aunt. Again, when all of the adults are busy scratching out a living, there's not much time for conflict. Circumstances remained as aforementioned; the only thing to change was the residence. These circumstances existed until I graduated from high school, completed two years of college, and joined the military at the age of eighteen.

Being born into deprivation had its advantages. You learned early to accept and appreciate what you had and to know the difference between necessities and luxuries. Reality was doing without some things—mostly convenience. Discipline, perseverance, and hard work were attributes that made it possible to get ahead. Those qualities, learned at an early age, were later applied to all the teaching "missions" we had at the Cooper Aerobics Center.

Physical Activity as a Means for Growing Up

You might ask, what do kids who don't have much (that's what the "condition" was called) do for fun—or play? We were in school for nine months of the year. School was absolutely phenomenal. We got a heavy dose of the three Rs in grammar school, which was grades one through seven. Our teachers were great and pillars of the community and known to all of our parents. We got plenty of the basics. More importantly to us, we got ample unsupervised playground time (recess). In the first four grades, we did lots of swinging, seesawing, and merry-go-rounding. The playground was rocky, with no grass and patches of goat heads (stickers) in some areas.

In the upper grades, we did lots of running, a little fun wrestling (not organized) and softball. One year our principal, Mr. Kennedy, organized us into football teams and allowed us to play tackle football under his supervision. These factors led naturally to the development of a love and appreciation for being outside, for activity and movement, and for testing my physical abilities.

School was fun, but we lived for summer. Summer meant *free range* roaming. In small towns, we had lots of "come and go" latitude very early in life. By the age of four or five, I was allowed to go between grandparents' homes or go to town alone for a manageable list of groceries. What did kids do who don't have much play with? We played lots of circle games, red rover, ante-over, hopscotch, jacks, capture the flag, all kinds of tag and hide-and-seek games and their many variations, stilt walking, rope jumping, and rubber guns. We threw rocks at almost everything that wouldn't break. We rolled old rubber tires almost everywhere.

Lots of time was spent in Mr. Bennett's pasture, which was just across the railroad tracks—about seventy-five yards away. We hunted with slingshots but never killed a thing. We crawfished in Mr. Bennett's stock tank—catch and release. Mom's only caveat was "Don't mess with the bull" in the pasture. I don't ever remember her saying, "Don't play on the railroad tracks when a train is coming" or "Don't go swimming in the stock tank." As we grew a little older, ten to twelve, we got together

174

or softball, touch or tackle football, or keep-away. There were no parks or playgrounds. The games were played on vacant lots with no adult supervision—ever. My early years centered around school, chores, and physical activity, most of which was outdoors. Being successful in the games we played reinforced my love of activity.

At the age of thirteen, I became a freshman in high school. We had seven years of grammar school and four years of high school. World War II was underway during most of my high school years. Conditions at home remained the same; school activities changed significantly. Our physical education classes consisted mostly of calisthenics and obstacle course running, preparing us for military service. Sports programs were limited, but we did have football, basketball, and track. We had one coach for all sports who was also the superintendent of schools. Sports consisted mostly of practice; not much traveling was done because of rationing and shortages of food, transportation, and personal commodities.

My freshman year I started to work at one of the local drug stores from 6:00 p.m. to 9:00 p.m. After school there was athletics until 5:00 p.m., then work from 6:00 until 9:00, then home to do what little homework I wasn't able to do at school. On Saturdays, I worked from 8:00 a.m. until 11:00 p.m. with forty-five minutes off for dinner and another forty-five minutes off for supper. I was paid twenty-five cents an hour. To believe it you had to have lived it. World War II ended in the fall of 1945, the beginning of my senior year.

With wartime restrictions ended, we were able to resume our athletic programs, including travel. As a senior, I was able to represent my high school in football, basketball, track, and tennis. We didn't have baseball. During our freshman year, we were required to take a course called Occupations/Civics—one semester of each. Today, Occupations might be called Career Counseling, and Civics would be Fundamentals of Government. Our teacher was a wonderful woman who had us consider and research two career paths that we might like to pursue after graduation from high school or college. After researching our two declared vocations, we were required to construct a notebook for each one, called Career Books, and designate a first and second choice. My choices were easy. Japan's unprovoked attack on Pearl Harbor almost dictated my first choice. Like most other young American boys, I wanted to serve my country, and I wanted to do it flying. My first career book was called simply *Navy Pilot*. My second choice came quite naturally as a result of the way I was allowed to grow. I had been given a lot of freedom to choose the activities of my interests. Outdoor, active pursuits were an easy choice. When I wasn't working, I was involved in play activities developing the skills and strength that led to success in athletic endeavors. Consequently, by the age of thirteen I knew I wanted to be a pilot or a physical education teacher/coach. Little did I know it at the time, but this all laid the groundwork for my career as a teacher that culminated at the Cooper Aerobics Center.

Preparing for a Career in Physical Education

All of our teachers acted as counselors and encouraged us to attend college. College wasn't a given for most graduates whose parents couldn't afford to pay tuition, room, board, and books. However, if you lived in a city or within commuting distance of a city with a university, you could commute to the university, live at home, and only have the expenses of tuition and books. Living fifteen miles from Waco made it possible to commute to Baylor University. Paying tuition on the installment plan, three installments a quarter, made tuition a little more affordable. We had no family car, but for a couple of bucks a week, I could ride with other car-owning commuters. In the mid-1940s, there were no SATs or ACTs, so enrolling at the university of your choice was rather uncomplicated if you were not living in the dormitory. You merely showed up with your high school transcript, expressed a desire to attend, and enrolled.

Graduating high school in May of 1946 at the age of sixteen made it possible for me to enroll at Baylor University in the fall of 1946, just after my seventeenth birthday. My major was HPER (Health, Physical Education, and Recreation). I loved my classes, my professors, and being involved in *my* course of study. In 1946 Baylor enjoyed enrolling one of its largest student bodies, almost thirteen hundred students, many of

176

whom were ex-GIs who were enrolling or reenrolling after World War I. They were receiving help with the well-deserved GI Bill, which paid tuition, books, and a stipend of ninety-five dollars a month, a fact that was not lost on us younger students. It was exciting to be immersed in a course of study that I loved so much and believed in so strongly.

In the spring quarter of 1948, the final quarter of my sophomore year, I found myself overextended. Course work, work, and involvement in extracurricular activities left me unable to focus on academics as I should. I was spread too thin, and money was in short supply. I reluctantly withdrew from school to concentrate on making more money. Working through the summer and fall of 1948 left me a little better off financially but not able to go back to school. During the fall of 1948, the North Korean conflict escalated significantly, and many young men my age were subject for conscription into military service. Volunteering for the service of your choice seemed better to me.

I enlisted in the US Coast Guard for a three-year hitch from December 1948 to December 1951. In 1951, the Korean situation was still dire, and all services were extended for a year. As the intensity of the conflict diminished, our extension was reduced to six months, leading to my discharge on June 6, 1952. I was trained as a medical corpsman, which gave me the real-world experience on the medical aspects of our physical nature and activity. In turn, that knowledge and skill set aided me in my work later on at the Cooper Aerobics Center.

Fulfillment as a Teacher

My plan was to work through the summer and reenroll at Baylor in the fall of 1952. Reenrolling as a more mature student with four years of world experience had its advantages. Tuition and books were paid for along with a ninety-five-dollar-a-month stipend. I was ecstatic. After receiving my bachelor of science degree in the spring of 1954, I was offered a teaching fellowship to work toward a master's degree, then I would join the faculty to teach physical education. Nothing could have made me happier.

In 1956, I became a faculty member, teaching until the fall of 1959. While university teaching has prestige and respectability, public school experience molds the educator. Therefore, in 1959, I accepted a position as coordinator (supervisor) of physical education and swim coach in the San Angelo Public Schools. Realizing the need for coordinators to be connected to the classroom, the school required that I teach two classes of physical education. It took less than a month for me to realize that university teaching was the ivory tower, and public school teaching and coaching were where the rubber meets the road.

At the end of nine years, I came to the conclusion that I was much better suited for teaching than administration. This conclusion led to setting two new goals: working toward an advanced degree and a return to college teaching. The opportunity came in 1967 with the offer of a teaching position in the Health, Physical Education, and Recreation Department at the University of Texas at El Paso, teaching university students how to navigate and implement successful careers in the discipline of HPER. Here is where public school teaching and coaching experience paid dividends. Summers off allowed me to begin work on an advanced degree. Each summer for three years was spent at the University of North Texas (UNT) taking courses fulfilling the requirements for the advanced degree. The academic year and summer of '71–'72 was spent in residence at UNT on a teaching fellowship as I finished my coursework for the degree, completing the process by passing oral and written exams and successfully preparing and defending the topic of my dissertation.

I returned to teaching at UTEP the academic year of '72–'73 and had completed collecting and analyzing data for my dissertation by the fall of '73. Teaching and writing the dissertation was a long, slow process, culminating in the awarding of the EdD degree in the spring of 1977. Continuing my teaching at the University of Texas at El Paso was very gratifying, as I was blessed with dedicated students and associated with professional colleagues.

Onward to the Cooper Aerobics Center

Each of us, at times in our lives, has identified events that happen as life-changing experiences. In 1982, after twenty-eight years of teaching, my life was about to change significantly. In midsummer of that year, I received a call from Dr. Charles Sterling, a longtime friend and colleague, who was CEO of the Cooper Institute for Aerobics Research in Dallas, Texas. As we visited, he explained that the institute was looking for a teacher in the Division of Continuing Education. He asked if I would be interested in interviewing for the position. My heart rate quickened, and my palms got sweaty; I tried not to appear too eager but said that I would be interested.

I held Dr. Cooper in the highest esteem, and high on my bucket list was to someday visit the center, get a tour, and observe professional excellence. After twenty-eight years of teaching, fifteen of which were at UTEP, my professional life was well established: associate professor—never to be professor because I didn't publish—great students, very professional and personable colleagues, and settled comfortably into my professional niche. At age fifty-two and professionally satisfied, many would not relish the challenge of change. But I did not have a second thought. I was subsequently interviewed and was offered and accepted the position.

For twenty-two wonderful years, I was privileged to work alongside the most remarkable and professional colleagues one could have. We shared common goals, values, attitudes, and beliefs. More importantly, we shared with our clients how important it was to develop an appreciation and enthusiasm for a forever-active lifestyle. A life of purposeful physical activity contributes to a modicum of physical fitness and level of wellness that may add years to your life and life to your years. Purposeful physical activity enhances functionality as well as longevity.

I've often wondered: Was my move to the Cooper Institute just serendipity, or was it providence? I don't know. I do know that it was a fitting end to a rewarding career, providing me with the opportunity to grow professionally, work with amazing colleagues, and serve humanity in ways I never thought possible. For these things, I am eternally grateful. I am also humbled to have been a small part of Dr. Cooper's phenomenal legacy.

Final Reflections

To many people retirement represents the end of the story. No longer engaged in professional activities, it is natural for one's attention to turn toward self-indulgence. For those of us in service professions, nothing could be further from the truth. If one feels called into a profession, beliefs and values are not changed by not being actively and formally engaged. Since retiring in 2004 at seventy-five years of age, my attitudes and beliefs over the years have been manifested in my actions. Never underestimate the impact you have on other people, not by what you say but by what you do. Seventeen years after retirement, my actions speak louder than my words. My friends and associates know that purposeful physical activity keeps me very functional and slows the process of aging. Modeling what you believe means addressing many questions and stimulating much discussion.

The members of my bicycle club (average age: early to mideighties) share my enthusiasm and love of riding and my belief in physical activity with a purpose. In my workout facility, people can see that older persons may exercise at higher levels of intensity for longer periods of duration without adverse side effects. My pastor has been convinced that he needs to stay fit and well to meet the demands of his stressful calling. He often reports to me what he is doing without being questioned. He and his wife ride with our bicycle club on occasion. Living my beliefs that exercise is medicine communicates that point to others without the formalities involved. It is just another method of using my gift as God intended.

Remember always to "live simply, love generously, care deeply, speak kindly...and leave the rest to God."

Addendum
Missionary Outreaches
Summary

Many organizations over the years were impacted by the Cooper Institute's services, which were described as "missionary outreaches" in this history. We would venture to say that no other organization in the world has provided the amount of physical fitness services directly to the number of diverse military, public safety, health, fitness, corporate wellness, educational, and health/fitness promotion entities that we did. To give a perspective on the scope of that body of work, below is a brief summary of the variety of organizations that benefited from the "missionary outreaches." It would be too lengthy to list all the groups, so only a few examples are given for each category of organization:

- All five US military services, including the Army, Navy, Air Force, Marine Corps, and Coast Guard

- Three foreign military services, including the British Royal Marines and the Swiss National Guard

- Nineteen federal law enforcement agencies, including the FBI, DEA, and Secret Service

- Thirty-one state police agencies, including the California Highway Patrol, New York State Police, and Texas Department of Public Safety

- 121 municipal police departments, including the Houston Police Department, Denver Police Department, and the New York Police Department

- Eighteen state Police Officer Standards and Training Councils (POSTS), including Arizona, Kentucky, and Wyoming

- Seven police officer associations, including the International Association of Chiefs of Police and the American Society of Law Enforcement Trainers

- Eight fire departments, including the Massachusetts Firefighters Training Council and the Dallas Fire Department

- Four federal Nuclear Regulatory Commission facilities, including Commonwealth Edison and Washington Public Power

- Eighty-nine community service sites, including the Boys and Girls Clubs of Illinois, the National YMCA, and the Illinois National Guard Drug Demand Reduction program armories

- Seventeen health clinics and hospitals, including the US Indian Health Service, Hospital Corporation of America, and Institute for Sports Medicine in Switzerland

- Twelve corporate wellness programs, including Encyclopedia Britannica and Aetna life insurance

- Ten health club/fitness centers, including Jack LaLanne European Health Spas and the Nihon Aerobics Center, Japan

- Twelve public school districts and higher educational institutions, including El Paso Community College, University of Missouri at Kansas City, and New York City schools

- Thousands of FitnessGram school sites plus all the schools in four states, including Texas and California

- Six national physical fitness and health promotion agencies, including the Presidents Council for Physical Fitness and Sports and the American College of Sports Medicine

Those organizations cited are only those groups that the institute provided direct contract services to. If we were to count the number of organizations represented by the students in our courses, that number would be in the thousands and would probably be reflective of organizations from about every country in the world. In addition would be the thousands of individual personal trainers who attended institute courses. In many respects the institute's personal trainer certification course became that industry's standard.

Acknowledgments

There are many individuals, too numerous to mention, who have influenced our lives and careers. We will just acknowledge those who have been our counselors, our sounding boards, and our soul mates. We are forever grateful for our wives, Gretchen, Annette, and Shirley, who have put up with us over the years. The efforts described in this history and memoir would never have happened without their loving support, insights, and patience. We also want to give a special thanks to Holly Collingwood, Tom's daughter-in-law, who served for us old guys as our needed computer guru.

Finally, we must acknowledge God. We believe there was a plan for us that, at times, we were not aware of. It wasn't luck or fate that brought us together or influenced the results. It was the result of what we believe was a divine plan. Give thanks to God.

CPSIA information can be obtained
at www.ICGtesting.com
Printed in the USA
BVHW060945200122
626629BV00016B/2314

9 781638 3777